PRAISE FOR
DOES THIS FEEL FAMILIAR?

"This is a must-read for anyone affected by an eating disorder in their family. It has invaluable insights and will resonate with any family member of someone who suffers or has suffered from an eating disorder. Written by non-clinicians, it is able to speak to where so many families find themselves—feeling alone, afraid, and totally overwhelmed."

Stephanie Setliff, M.D.
Medical Director | Eating Recovery Center of Dallas

"This book is thoughtful and insightful. From the perspective of patients and families, it takes you through the spectrums of fears, mistakes, panic, hope, and finally the possibilities of recovery. After sixteen years in the field, it is wonderful to have such a direct and candid look into the experiences of treatment and recovery of eating disorders. This collected work will guide you through the path taken by so many others, and to know that you are not alone in the darkness."

Tyler Wooten, M.D.
Medical Director | Eating Recovery Center of Dallas

"*Does This Feel Familiar?* is equal parts raw, poignant, emotional, and powerful. I love that the treasure trove of stories, advice and solutions does not come from an 'expert' in the field, but from the voices of the real experts: Moms. Many Moms. As well as their loved ones. Excellent, excellent, potent, potent, excellent."

Eddie Coker
Singer/Songwriter
Founder of The Wezmore Project

"Dearest family, friends, acquaintances, and strangers, this book is for you. *Does This Feel Familiar?* is for anyone who *loves* someone struggling."

A Mom

DOES THIS FEEL FAMILAR?

DOES THIS FEEL FAMILIAR?

For Mothers of Children **Struggling** with an **Eating Disorder**

written by a collection of families, friends, and brave survivors

Fedd Books
P.O. Box 341973
Austin, TX 78734
www.thefeddagency.com

Published in association with The Fedd Agency, Inc., a literary agency.

The opinions and conclusions expressed in this book are those of the author(s). All references to websites, blogs, authors, publications, brand names, and/or products are placed there by the author.

This publication is designed to provide accurate and authoritative information with regard to the subject matter covered. It is sold with the understanding that the publisher or author is not engaged in rendering medical or other professional advice. If expert assitance is required, the services of a competent professional should be sought.

ISBN: 978-1-943217-49-6
eISBN: 978-1-943217-50-2

Printed in the United States of America
First Edition 15 14 13 10 09 / 10 9 8 7 6 5 4 3 2

This book is dedicated to:

The child whose profound struggle became our window to the world uniting a family with a bond that cannot be broken.

The sister and brother who felt alone at times but purposefully chose love and the risk of loving won.

The mom and dad who fought beyond reason and would do it all over again to save the life of their child.

The extended family who opened their home and to those who showed up and held the foundation in hand when others were exhausted, confused, and/or scared.

The wingman who loved us just as we were.

The friends and mentors who offered comfort without judgment.

The young man who believed in the light and goodness of our child's soul.

The neighbors who supportively held our village strong.

The doctors who have chosen to dedicate their lives to the health and well-being of our children.

And to the honest people who have chosen to share their hearts in this book.

A portion of the proceeds from this book will be dedicated to help those who cannot afford treatment.

"You will be tested; you will be pushed to what you think is your limit. At times you will break. Motherhood isn't a job; it is a part of who you are. I'm a mom.

You will stumble and at times want to run away, but you won't. You will find you're resilient . . . And yes, you will second-guess your wisdom. 'Am I doing this right? Am I equipping this special child with what they need to address this ever-changing world?'

As time passes you'll realize it's not about molding your child into the person you think they should become; it's about finding out who they are, encouraging their strengths, and loving them through their weaknesses.

You'll be surprised at how different a child from your womb seems, and those differences can cause you immeasurable anxiety. But you'll come to realize your child is like you. And it's through the eyes of that child that you will learn about yourself and about life."

- A MOM

TABLE OF CONTENTS

Section Four: What's the Bigger Picture?

FOREWORD

"I have an eating disorder." "My daughter has an eating disorder." "My husband has an eating disorder." "My wife has an eating disorder." "My grandson has an eating disorder." "My mother has an eating disorder." "My roommate has an eating disorder." "My best friend has an eating disorder."

If any of these statements sound familiar and are true for you, then this book, written by individuals who have experienced the extreme challenges faced by their loved one having an eating disorder, will be a valuable resource.

If you are someone who has anorexia nervosa, bulimia nervosa, or binge-eating disorder, then you know firsthand how all-encompassing and possibly life-threatening these disorders can be. And those who love you, who are in the trenches with you, battling the eating disorder as best they can for and with you, struggle with their own pain as they watch you in the midst of your suffering.

Everyone who comes in contact with an eating disorder struggles for control. Control over body. Control over food. Control over feelings. Control over others. Control: deeply desired, terribly elusive.

The authors of this book—who have chosen to speak in "one voice" but who are all deeply impacted by the various eating disorders—want you to have the wisdom they have gained through experience. They want you <u>not</u> to have to start at square one when you hear a professional say, "I think your child (you and/ or your family member) has an eating disorder." They want you <u>not</u> to feel alone as you start on the journey toward recovery—an often very long and arduous journey that can feel confusing, overwhelming, circuitous, and never-ending.

Each chapter in the book stands on its own; read in the order presented or pick and choose based on what you need help with the most urgently. The testimonials at the end of each chapter give a candid glimpse into the life of someone who has personally been affected by an eating disorder.

If you are a parent or caretaker for someone you love struggling with the complexities of striving to recover from an eating disorder, this book has been lovingly written to provide you support, understanding, resources, care, and concern. As a psychologist specializing in the treatment of eating disorders for over thirty-five years, I can attest to how much effort is required by everyone involved to help someone with an eating disorder heal. *Does This Feel Familiar?* offers each reader hope for a recovered future.

Betty K. Armstrong, Ph.D.
Clinical Psychologist

THE PURPOSE OF
DOES THIS FEEL FAMILIAR?

Does This Feel Familiar? is created by moms who chose to work anonymously and collectively, speaking in "one voice" because this is a story about all maternal beings. With the help of notable medical doctors combined with the testimonials and opinions of our children and family members, we aim to increase your knowledge about eating disorders.

By combining our voices, *Does This Feel Familiar?* emerges from the female psyche rather than the individual circumstances that often separate us. We, as women and mothers, share similar experiences and therefore have compassion for your journey and what is to come. Is there really a difference between a hipster mom, a helicopter mom, a working mom, a soccer mom, or the drama mom? Perhaps. But not when it comes to our children. There is a common thread that resides in all of us, no matter the physical boundaries, socio-economic status, race, creed, political opinion, or wealth; the hopes, dreams, and prayers for our children are universally the same.

The purpose of this book is to aggregate and condense new and innovative ideas, as well as existing schools of thought, to help you during the educational phase of your journey. We want to share our successes and our failures, and in doing so, help you to understand that this is life; we've got to come together and face the challenges.

There is a plethora of information on eating disorders available to parents: hundreds of informative websites, books, doctors, therapists, nutritionists, and treatment centers. These resources are all valuable, and yet, they often feel overwhelming. It is our hope that by condensing the vast amount of information into this short collection of personal thoughts and research, we will help you become more productive and focused.

The appendix in this book will give you referrals, answers, and tangible places to start or further your education. *Does This Feel Familiar?* can be read cover to cover or modularly depending on where you are personally in the journey. Additionally, this material is intended to help you decipher, identify, and practically manage your discomfort. It is written modularly, so you can pick and choose what works for you and/or read it from top to bottom.

We do not have all the answers, but we can tell you what worked and has helped our child, our entire family, and ourselves.

And perhaps most importantly, this book was created to remind us all that, even in the darkest of times, it is crucial that we vigorously trust our wisdom, believing that there is always hope for whole and comprehensive healing. What does that really mean? Recovery is about allowing yourself to be human—imperfect and free from the lies of an eating disorder. Recovery is not about becoming the perfect person (or having a perfect relationship with food). Recovery is about knowing and accepting that you—whether you are a victim of an eating disorder or not—are worthy.

Worthy of life, worthy of love, and worthy of self-reliance.

Please allow us to help you help yourself, as we are made stronger together in knowledge.

INTRODUCTION

Knowledge enhances our rational thinking during times of consequential crossroads.

Over the years I've been asked, "What do you feel?" "How does this make you feel?" "What are you feeling?" Most of the time I was unable to find the words to verbalize the depth of my emotion—scared, angry, frustrated, and often inept. And, at times I felt numb, blank, incapable, exposed, and honestly, there were moments I was simply just too tired to identify how I felt. I vividly remember feeling paralyzed with fear, the dark fear of losing a child. Questioning myself in uncertainty wondering, *why can't I fix my child's eating disorder?*

Above all, I am a mother, and mothers believe that we can restore and mend what is broken, especially in our very own children. Each child is different, and thus each journey is different and customized to that child's needs. No one really understands the plight of the parent-child relationship except one's own self. I have a connection some don't understand. We've been told it is too deep, too close. I don't believe that, and all I care about is that my little girl understands who we are as mom and daughter. What does it take for her to feel safe and unconditionally loved? What will it take for her to understand us? Am I willing to put in the hours it takes to define our relationship?

What seems unusual or disconcerting to others may have layers of work and understanding that only a child and that parent share. As a parent, we give more of ourselves than we thought capable. Our own children take us to places we did not know we were capable of going—dimensions we step into, dimensions we step out of, and dimensions we now reside in. It's our own children who are often our door to the universe. The real truths lie within the walls of our own homes. The real truths are the "hows." I sometimes wonder if I handled each "how" error-free. Was it guided in love, respect, and understanding to the best of my ability at that time? If we had our way, there would be things we would change. But we do not have that luxury. Time halts for no one. The passage of time is guaranteed; we cannot turn the clock back.

Precious time went by too quickly, and I often felt like I was stuck in reverse. Not necessarily powerless, just ineffective. I wanted someone to understand. I wanted someone to rescue my child, to rescue my family, and to rescue me. I desperately wanted someone to tell me what to do. This is what it felt like to be the mother of a child in the grip of an eating disorder. The journey I planned was not working! Does this feel familiar?

The bond and unconditional love between mother and child is as ancient as history itself. Perhaps maternal love is the most intoxicating, powerful emotion on earth. It can destroy you, or it can make you stronger. We do have the choice. I had to reshape some of my own understandings.

It took a few years of floundering until I made a connection with a therapist, and thus, my own heart. I allowed myself to be vulnerable and to not hide. I chose to be open, to be honest, to educate myself, and to become proactive as an advocate for my child, my family, and myself. I learned to follow the advice of professionals, other mothers, parents, and my own intuition. I not only heard but I chose to *listen*. During this process I experienced a turning point where I knew, no matter how wearisome, exhausting, or difficult, I would never give up on my child. Love prevails. Hope is victorious. And we, all of us, will do this together.

The words and pages that follow are written in humility and endearment for all mothers and caretakers in hopes they may discover what they feel, what they know, how they will proceed, and what choices they will make on behalf of their family and selves. When asked, "What is it like to be the mother of a child with an eating disorder?" you will be able to answer with knowledge and confidence. We aspire to help you answer this question and more.

– A Mother

HOW DOES YOUR CHILD REALLY FEEL?

"This life isn't about me. But that's not what I'm
told by the million messages that unfold on T.V.
I am a soul . . . I have a body. Yet tuck, nip, trim,
diet, starve lend me to think perfection should be
my new hobby. For "never enough, never enough"
is what the media whispers in my ear . . . through
the self-medicated self-abuse that leads to an
inability to hear truth. Caught up in lies, I run to
the arms of the culture . . . desperate for an affir-
mation of love. If I can change this, or if I alter
that, will it be enough?"

**– Diary of a Teen in the Depths of
an Eating Disorder**

1
WHAT MAKES YOU THINK THERE'S AN EATING DISORDER?

Listen to your intuition; it is trying to tell you something. There is knowledge in one's own intuition, most especially when your gut is telling you that something is not right with your child.

Begin by asking yourself, "Is there a problem?"

If you believe there is a problem, what makes you think that your child has an eating disorder?

Below is an email sent to a psychologist regarding a teenage child's unfamiliar behavior and the mom's worry. You can feel the mother's concern, and it seems almost all mothers can identify with the idea that "something just is not right!" We can't always find the words, but we know the gut feeling.

"There is a very steady pattern that happens when she drops to a certain weight (as she presently has). This monster comes at her like a wicked demon. She is irrational, obsessive and irritable . . . cries a lot, easily frustrated,

cannot sleep, is not engaged in the present and she fights herself. She fights me. She tends to make logic out of illogical situations or thoughts and yet, she can fool most anyone with her poise. Of course, her family sees it daily and just recently, through tears of frustration, she admitted to the power this demon has over her right now but still cannot hear with a clear mind. Since birth, her personality has been packed with emotions, it is what makes her a passionate compassionate person. I understand she is thirteen with all the hormones and such, but as her mom I know the difference. There is something terribly wrong yet, I cannot identify the exact problem. I think she is in trouble and we need to consider a concentrated treatment plan. What are your thoughts?"

— An Email to a Therapist from a Mom

Are there moments when you look at your child and do not recognize him or her—not only in a physical sense, but also in their behavior? Do you feel like she/he does not hear you? Do you feel like your conversations often get convoluted? Do you know your child needs help but are not sure what that means?

"As her mom, I know she needs more professional help versus confiding in me, lately it ends up in a tremendously frustrating place for us both. I am not even sure how that happens! I keep wondering what I did wrong. Perhaps she needs to be put in treatment or you can advise us on how much she needs to see you on a regular schedule. I will

work it out with her school . . . She needs more help, we need more help—can we please talk this afternoon? By this email I'm sure you can tell my level of frustration. I'm working to release my worries to God Almighty and remain proactive on our daughter's behalf but I am floundering. I have watched too many mothers pretend their child is perfect and look the other way. Or just write the behavior off as a "phase." We are not willing to pretend everything is "perfect" with our precious child. We need help and your suggestions. Please consider seeing (our child) several times over the next week and then, will you please meet with my husband and me?"

— An Email to a Therapist from a Mom

If you have experience with an eating disorder—whether it's a loved one who is the victim or yourself—we urge you to move forward in getting help and dealing directly with the issue at hand. This book is written modularly, so feel free to skip to the chapters containing information you are seeking.

If you do not have experience with an eating disorder, then now is the best time for an education. Statistics prove that the earlier the intervention, the highest possible probability of full recovery and healing.

What Could a Mom Do Now?

Please read through the suggestions below. We hope they help you recognize and better understand the behaviors and symptoms you are witnessing in your child. You are most likely reading this book because of your concern for a loved one—to either help you decipher if it is an eating disorder and/or if you know it is, then to help you gather facts and necessary knowledge. These three categories should help:

- Learn the Behavior Characteristics of an Eating Disorder
- Learn the Terms and Definitions of Eating Disorders
- Learn the "Truths" about Eating Disorders

Learn the Behavior Characteristics of an Eating Disorder

There is an obvious change in the behavior of a person with an eating disorder. Your maternal radar will warn you that something is *not* right with your child. Eventually, you will find the behavioral changes shocking, as the child you felt you knew so well will confuse you. For a period of time your child can hide these traits, but eventually they surface. These behaviors are most often adopted as a means to cope with the psychological struggles your child is going through. Keep in mind that the first six characteristics of the following list are also often used to hide symptoms.

These are characteristics of the disease, not your child. The core of your precious child is still there. A good rule of thumb is: Get mad at the disease, not the person! Fight the disease, not the person.

Withdrawn	Less social. Pensive. Pushes friends, parents, and loved ones away.
Manipulative	Attempts to control situations so they get their way. Twists stories and situations to hide their disordered behaviors.

Avoidance	Finds excuses why they can't be with others. Avoids questions or confrontation with those who question activities and behavior.
Controlling	Manipulates situations in order to contain/control their world and structure it the way they want.
Dishonest	Lies. Does not reveal full truths. Hides the truth. Manipulates the truth.
Sneaky	Secretive.
Short-tempered	Agitated. Irritable. Replies with short answers to get you off their back.
Disrespectful	Rude in both actions and verbal response. Ill-mannered. Unnaturally impolite. Flippant.
Emotional	Temperamental. Reactionary outside of typical sensitivity.
Volatile	Quick to anger. Emotionally and physcally abusive.
Teary	Quick to cry.
Weary	Physically tired. Exhausted. Fatigued. Slugglish.
Depressed	Sad. Heavy-hearted. Depression is very common in eating disorders.
Egocentric	Obsessed with eating disorder, thus the eating disorder is obsessed with them. Selfish. Self-centered.
Anxiety	Anxiety is the most common characteristic. It can be the onset of an eating disorder and/or the inherent anxiety existed before the disease. Some of the typical co-existing disorders with an anxiety

component are obsessive-compulsive, social anxiety, and panic attacks.

> *"I find comfort that when my child is "being selfish" I can now understand that the behavior is part of the mental illness process. It is a symptom, not a reflection, of my child."*
> — Mom of a Child Suffering from Anorexia

Learn the Terms and Definitions of Eating Disorders

Mothers and caregivers need to learn and understand eating-disorder vocabulary. They must recognize the signs and symptoms of the disease and be educated when speaking to professionals. If you are familiar with eating disorders, feel free to skip this section.

There are many categories used to explain the variety of eating disorders. If you're just beginning the education process, please approach your education intently and not hastily. The vast amount of information is overwhelming at first.

The four primary eating disorders we are going to focus on are the most common with subsets in each area: Anorexia Nervosa (AN), Bulimia Nervosa (BN), Binge-eating Disorder (BED), and Other Specified Feeding and Eating Disorders (OSFED). These are the four disorders we hear the most about.

Below you will find our descriptions in laymen's terms from what we have seen and experienced as caregivers.

For the diagnostic criteria as categorized by the American Psychiatric Association, Diagnostic and Statistical Manual of Mental Disorders (DSMV) and more specific and detailed definitions, please refer to the appendix in the back of the book. We have put information in the appendix that might feel a little tedious, but it's important to follow and interpret medical verbiage when healing from an eating disorder.

Anorexia Nervosa (AN)

Individuals with anorexia have distorted body images and a fear of gaining weight. Disturbingly, their brains actually see their own reflection as abnormally heavy, a skewed body dysmorphia. This fear is characterized by self-starvation, restricting and controlling food intake, and overindulgent exercise. Sometimes the "obvious starving body" is not as apparent, but the abnormal behaviors based around food topics, weight, body image, and/or self-esteem are alarming. Anorexia Nervosa has the highest death risk of any psychiatric disorder—more than twice that of depression, schizophrenia, and/or bi-polar disease. It is most frightening for a parent when they realize young adults diagnosed with anorexia in their twenties face an even higher rate of probable death.

This illness is a mental sickness that aims to fully control the mind of our loved ones. It lies to them, and in turn, they lie to themselves and others.

> *"I knew my parents were concerned that I wasn't eating enough, so I insisted nothing was wrong—I was fine, and I hid things from them. I would purposefully eat something in front of my mom just so she'd think I was eating, and then I'd punish myself by restricting the rest of the day. I eventually lost interest in things I had been passionate about. Looking back, it was as if I had sold myself to the eating disorder, and it was my master."*
>
> – Reflecting Back

The mental illness is equally severe physically, as anorexia can cause medical complications such as heart dysfunction, hair loss, bone loss, skin discoloration, and more. Whether we call it a disease or disorder, anorexia is extremely serious and should be addressed immediately because we know the best results for healing come from an early intervention. If you want more details on the description of anorexia, please refer to the appendix in the back of this book. Anorexia Nervosa comes from Latin words that mean "nervous inability to eat."

Bulimia Nervosa (BN)

The eating disorder, Bulimia Nervosa, is an emotional disorder characterized by an individual's response to their perceived overabundant intake of food. We say perceived because it is the discretion of the individual as to how much is too much when eating food. A person with Bulimia Nervosa often "binge-eats" by consuming large quantities of food (insatiable overeating) then vomits what they have eaten to rid their body of the calories consumed in false hope of losing weight because they have poor body-image issues. Sadly, the individual is ashamed of his or her behavior, so they sneak food in private, causing more guilt and self-ridicule. Similar to anorexia, there are issues with body dysmorphia, low self-love, poor body image, depression, and anxiety.

There are two common subtypes of bulimia. Purging is when the individual induces vomiting to rid their body of food as a result of what they consider excessive overeating, and/or they take laxatives, diuretics, and/or self-administered enemas. The second common subtype is called non-purging. To deal with an individual's compulsive overeating they compensate with bouts of fasting and/or excessive exercise. The ill-judged behavior towards self and eating is abnormal and dangerous from a mental and medical standpoint. If you want more details about Bulimia Nervosa, please refer to the appendix in the back of this book.

> *"During one of the first IOP parent meetings I ever attended (and I ended up going to many) I found myself sitting in a room with nine other parents discussing our children's eating disorder cases. One mom explained her child's bulimia and what really hit home were two things: one, she did not know for several years, and two, when she began to suspect something was really wrong she began looking for clues. What she found shocked me then but now I realize it is not abnormal. This mom said she found a drawer full of Ziploc baggies with vomit in each one! During the following weeks and months, she would find up to twelve Ziploc baggies full of vomit that were hidden in various drawers, under the bed, in her car, and in the alley trash can. The discovery opened the family up for a long journey of healing yet the mom had a tremendous amount of guilt. During these parent meetings she would often hang her head and say, 'How could I have not known this?'"*
>
> – A Surprised Mom

All of us—each and every one of the women who has been a part of writing this book—have been surprised and even shocked by our child's behavior. It comes with the territory. But, we have also worked hard to move beyond those lightning bolts and, probably most importantly, we have learned not to judge our loved one for it. A person struggling with bulimia does not need to be shamed; they already feel shameful. They need to be loved. Loving them means addressing the issue and finding help as they learn to help themselves.

Binge-eating Disorder (BED)

To binge means to indulge in an activity of excess. Binge-eating disorder is when an individual indulges in repetitive, excessive overeating often with a feeling of not being able to stop. These episodes can become ritualistic odd behavior around food and meals, hiding their overeating habits from loved ones, eating alone, and/or hoarding food. The ritual of eating to excess is most always followed with disgust of self. This loss of control promotes physical discomfort accompanied by shame and disappointment. Weight gain may not be obvious and/or can cause obesity. The less physically obvious, but equally scary, is the unseen depression, self-hate, and suicidal thoughts.

Why would our loved ones binge-eat? One reason is that, chemically, it feels good. Certain foods such as fats and sugars trigger the brain to release dopamine (the organic chemical of pleasure and reward). Compulsive eating helps to cover pain, social anxiety, loneliness, and sadness. But when people start binging for comfort, no one plans on it becoming a significant and destructive disorder they lose control over.

Other Specified Feeding and Eating Disorders (OSFED)

Other Specified Feeding and Eating Disorders (OSFED) is when an individual is in distress due to an eating disorder but whose characteristics do not fit within the DSMV's strict criteria for anorexia, bulimia, or binge-eating disorder. OSFED used to be called Eating Disorder Not Otherwise Specified (EDNOS). This diagnosis serves as a catch-all and encompasses a varied group of individuals. It can be the gateway to more severe eating disorder behavior, and yet a diagnosis of OSFED can be just as clinically severe, causing unwanted medical concerns. Distorted body image and/or over-valuation of shape and weight and/or an intense fear of gaining weight are shared characteristics of OSFED, anorexia, bulimia, and binge-eating. OSFED is the most common eating disorder and is a diagnosis for adolescents and adults affecting all people. In many ways it is also the most confusing when diagnosed. OSFED can feel vague and too open-ended and yet, the underlying emotional symptoms are congruent with other well-defined eating disorders. Therefore, seeking immediate help is consequential.

All eating disorders share the unkind quality of self-ridicule and often self-loathing. All eating disorders have obvious and

For more information or definitions outside of the categories above, please refer to the appendix in the back of this book for the appropriate resources. For suggestions on how to obtain professional help please refer to chapters 7 and 8 about getting professional help.

unseen characteristics that are harmful to the point of death. All eating disorders also have a high risk of simultaneous psychiatric disorders.

All eating disorders are treatable, and there is hope for healing.

We as caretakers often ask ourselves, *How in the world is it possible to overeat to the point of vomiting? Why don't they just stop? Why and how is it possible that my loved one is starving herself? Why don't they just eat?* We wonder about these odd behaviors around food. We feel confused and can't believe it is our child! Getting stuck in the vacuum of denial, confusion, guilt, blame, or ridicule will slow down the healing process. The answers may or may not be formidable in the beginning, but the most important thing to do is immediately reach out for first-rate help. Your questions may be answered eventually. But honestly, from experience, we can tell you that sometimes, after full and comprehensive healing, there still are unanswered questions. Sometimes in this life there are not adequate answers to questions we so desperately want to know. Being at peace without always having an answer is part of being human.

Getting educated is a wonderful decision.
Loving unconditionally is restorative.

Realities We Know to be True with Eating Disorders

There are many misconceptions about eating disorders. Unless you've had experiences with eating disorders, they can be very difficult to understand. Honestly, the most experienced of moms still find it complicated at times. Just like each person's thumbprint is unique, each eating-disorder case has its own personal triggers, traits, and behaviors. Below are eighteen truths about eating disorders that we feel are important for you to know.

- *You are not alone.* There are thousands and thousands of other families seeking help for their loved one struggling with an eating disorder. According to NEDA (National Eating Disorders Association) there has been an unprecedented growth of eating-disordered individuals in the last two decades. Up to 95 percent of those suffering are between the ages of twelve and twenty-six.[1] Those are our children. Each of those children has parents and hopefully families who love them. You are not alone in this battle—reach out for help. Please refer to the appendix in the back of this book for referrals.

> *"In the Unites States alone, 20 million women and 10 million men suffer from a clinically significant eating disorder at some point in their lives. The scope and severity of eating disorders are often misunderstood as they are serious complex illnesses, not lifestyle choices. They stem from issues beyond food and body size, and signify an attempt to control something of substance in an individual's life. They are the most complex and deadly of any mental/psychological disorder."[2]*
>
> *– Choose Life, Find Joy*

- *Healing is possible.* The earlier the disorder is caught and dealt with, the higher the potential for success. Though eating disorders are the most life-threatening of all psychiatric illnesses, there is hope for recovery. The essence of full recovery is when one learns to honestly love himself/herself both physically and emotionally and find worth in his/her existence. The simple but deeply complicated "golden rule" and/or summary of religious law

1. Smolak, 2011. "Get The Facts On Eating Disorders." National Eating Disorders Association. www.nationaleatingdisorders.org/prevalence-and-correlates-eating-disorders-adolescents N.p., n.d. Web. 07 Nov. 2016.

2. "NEDA Walk – Help Save Lives." Choose Life Find Joy. N.p., 21 Apr. 2016. Web. 09 Nov. 2016. www./neda.nationaleatingdisorders.org.

is: Love your neighbor as yourself. It does not say just to love yourself. It does not say to just love your neighbor. The bottom line is that positive self-esteem and acceptance of oneself is key to healing.

"If at thirteen you had told me where I would be now, at twenty-four . . . I wouldn't have believed you. I wouldn't have believed that I would appreciate and be abundantly grateful for my body and all that it can do. I wouldn't have believed that exercise would be an option for pleasure vs. a ritual necessary for bodily control. I wouldn't have believed that I could walk into any room knowing that I matter and that I have something to offer this world. I wouldn't have believed that I would be able to enjoy dessert on a date. I wouldn't have believed that I could stop calorie counting. I wouldn't have believed that I would care more about others well-being than their perception of me."

— Recovered and Living a Blessed Life

- *People with eating disorders are not selfish.* People dealing with an eating disorder do become obsessive compulsive over their own self. It's part of the disease. The clinically ill often seems selfish, but it's the disease that is selfish, not the person.

"It took me a while to understand what an eating disorder was; still not sure I totally get it! When my niece was in the depths of

an eating disorder her behavior seemed selfish and self-centered. I was frustrated witnessing the behavior and surprised it actually knocked my sister off center. I saw it as destructive to my sister and her immediate family. At the time I wondered, How in the world could such a brilliant, kind kid do such a selfish thing? But then I came to realize that my precious niece had a real problem. Her intention was not to hurt my sister, or anyone for that matter. She was slave to a complicated disease and it's a deep and very heavy subject. Grasping the overwhelming emotional toil, I offered for my niece to come live with us and seek day treatment in the city in which my family lives. It was in those months that I learned how emotionally crippling the struggle was for my niece. She was not being selfish, she was fighting for her life."

— An Aunt and Witness

- *People with anorexia are not always strikingly skinny.* Some might visually look sick, but this is not true for everyone who suffers. There are many factors to consider like body shape, genetics, metabolic rate, and metabolism. On the outside, they may look "normal" according to our Western/societal standards. But they are dying internally—both physically and emotionally.
- *The core of an eating disorder is driven by underlying issues.* It is not just about food. Eating is one of the few things a person can control; thus, they cover the pain through behaviors of not eating, overeating, and/or binge-eating.

"Though it goes against everything you understand, you have to realize that in most cases, this struggle is not about body image or weight or food. The obsession with exercise or food—be it over-eating or under-eating—is at its root a coping strategy, a way to cope with something much deeper. For me, it was about control.

I've always been more of a type-A, anxious, orderly and disciplined person. From what seemed like out of just boredom, my ED was almost something to be pre-occupied with, to work at, to practice, and to feel accomplished with when I saw that number on the scale 10 pounds lower, when someone commented on my thin frame.

I had a very healthy home environment where I felt loved and encouraged and beautiful as I was. So, when I told people it was about control, they assume my life was spinning out of control. It wasn't. I believe that nurturing this obsession was a way for my 15-year-old self, insecure at my core and seeking worth, to find a sense of identity and meaning."

– A Teenager's Desire for Control

- *Parents do not cause their child's eating disorder.* However, a parent's actions can result in a child's development of an eating disorder to cope. We are responsible for helping influence our child's healthy attitude about eating, body image, weight, and weight management. A positive influence is vitally important in their recovery.

- *Anybody can have an eating disorder, no matter gender, race, sexual preference, socioeconomic status, and/or religion.* According to ANAD (The National Association of Anorexia Nervosa and Associated Disorder), "In reality, no ethnic, gender or socioeconomic group is immune to the dangers of this disease. In regards to gender, 1.5 in 10 cases of these disorders involve males." [3]

- *Primary care physicians and pediatricians can miss the diagnosis of your child's eating disorder.* It is fair to say many miss the diagnosis because the body naturally compensates, which means the labs and vitals can read normal. A person's low weight and thin body might fit within the low range of our societal standards. It is deceiving. Have your loved one assessed by an eating-disorder specialist. Listen to your intuition. You know your child better than anyone else!

- *Eating disorders are not just a phase in a child's development.* Eating disorders are a serious, potentially fatal, brain disorder. Though different for each individual, research suggests that eating disorders persist for five to ten years and potentially a lifetime if not treated. Delay in getting treatment can often impact the longevity of an eating disorder.

- *A parent and/or caregiver cannot fix a loved one's eating disorder alone.* We highly recommend caregivers ask for support from loved ones or experienced friends. Seek professional help to become better equipped in dealing with the eating disorder behaviors and your child's underlying emotional frustrations.

- *An eating disorder is not contagious.* However, there are predisposed genes that can be inherent from biological family members who have or had an eating disorder, especially first generation, like parents.

---

3. "ANAD • National Association of Anorexia Nervosa and Associated Disorders." National Association of Anorexia Nervosa and Associated Disorders. N.p., n.d. Web. 09 Nov. 2016. www.anad.org.

- *There is ALWAYS a change in behavior with food.*
- *A person in the throws of an eating disorder, or recovering, does not remember all conflicts the same as you.* We all live life from our own point of view, our own perspective. A brain deprived of nutrition does not perceive life the same as you. When a person is in the depths of an eating disorder, their perception is altered, but that perception is as true to them as your truths are to you. So here are two thoughts we would like to share: 1) cognitive behavioral therapy is extremely helpful to sort out thoughts and patterned behavior and 2) even if you do not agree with the other person's perception, validating their pain and feelings is important. Pain and feelings are different than palpable memories.

"Memory? Truths? There are things she does not remember. Is that normal with anorexia? She tells me things I have said, things my husband has said and . . . to my knowledge they just are not my truths. Does anorexia hear our words and manipulatively twist them into a weapon causing shame, victimization, hurt, and the feeling of being misunderstood? Our child with anorexia has a brilliant mind with an amazing memory. But our memories can be so very different! Does she feel so much shame at

Or, is it just that I am not privy to some of her truths? Am I wrong in what I remember? As she matures will she remember differently? Is it a gift not to remember everything so she can let go of the shame? Maybe I am the one who is wrong! Maybe this is where forgiveness begins."

– A Confused Mom

- *Initially, no one chooses an eating disorder.* However, at some point in your child's recovery, he or she will have the choice to engage in eating-disorder behaviors or to fight their urge to.
- *The ripple effect from an eating disorder is inevitable.* When a loved one is victim to this hideous disease, everyone in his or her inner circle is affected, most especially the immediate family unit.

A Brother's Thoughts

Dear Friends,

I am a brother to a big sister that struggled with an eating disorder. The truth is that a "monster" casted itself over my sister and began to take control of how she viewed herself. Not only physically but mentally as well. After long years of torment, that I felt and personally watched, I have some things I would love to share.

- *Don't judge your sister for any problems but instead, try to remember that the beauty she had before the illness is still within her.*
- *Understand that there is a time to be a pusher and there is a time to be a listener.*
- *Don't be afraid to be in uncomfortable situations with your sibling who struggles with the problem. Because for damn sure they are uncomfortable all the time.*
- *Understand that there are unmet needs and focus on how you can help meet the needs of the hurting individual.*

Therapy helps.

- *There will be a lot of guilt and shame in the individual's heart. Be okay with sitting in that guilt with them and try to make sure she/he does not push to extremes to have revenge over their body.*
- *Know the struggle within yourself is real. The pain you feel is harsh and at times only sharpens. Don't be afraid to be vulnerable with the ones you love cause the weight is too heavy. Try to share the burden.*
- *The battle is real but, in order to fight fairly, you need to be still with yourself and strengthen your own heart.*
- *Accept the individual for who they really are because at the end of the day they have just as much worth as all people.*
- *Most importantly is to love unconditionally and let them know you love them no matter what!!!*

Honestly I could go on for hours as this has impacted my life greatly. Just know that every moment you see a sign of worth being restored in the sick individual, be joyful and fight for more times like that. There is no pain like it and it's a hell of a ride.

— A Brother Who Was Just Eight Years Old
When the Battle Began

- *An eating disorder is not healed by affirming one's outward appearance.* To the contrary, it can be very harmful. Try commenting on your child's internal beauty and empower their purpose, not their looks.

> *"When you comment on how thin she is, even if you mean it negatively (trying to show her she doesn't need to lose any more weight) it feeds the eating disorder. It's backwards and it doesn't make sense, but what she will take from that is, "It's working and I like this feeling. My attempt to control my weight and food is working and I'm going to pursue it even further."*
>
> — A Fifteen-Year-Old

- *It is not just about the food!* We will say this several times throughout the book and want to be clear about this statement. Restoring weight to a starving body is critical. The mind cannot function properly until the intake of adequate nutrition balances the brain. Once nutrition is balanced, the underlying issues have to be addressed, as well as the mental disorder's constant mantra of self-hatred and worthlessness. Comprehensive healing is when love finally prevails, and an individual's self-worth, purpose, and self-love is restored.

- *Individuals suffering from an eating disorder have distorted perception.* They do not view themselves the way others physically see them, nor do they think with a clear and level-headed mind.

> *"I didn't need people to tell me I was beautiful. I didn't need people to tell me I was the perfect size. I needed people*

to tell me that I wasn't alone and that I wasn't the only one fighting this. Let's be clear. I'm not talking about the eating disorder. Obviously, I knew lots of others struggled with eating disorders but not me. I didn't think I had one. What I'm talking about is war waging within me. I'm talking about the battle with the monster inside my mind that told me he had a way to control the insecurities and anxieties that seemed to weave together in an entanglement of chaos and destruction. Know that my eating disorder had nothing to do with the world around me rather, my distorted perception of the world around me. It is for that reason that I want you to know that you are not a failure. You and your loved one can survive this and when you make it to the other side there will be life after that survival. Love wins and in the end that's all anyone really has to offer. I wanted it to describe the idea that the people around me were the problem. The problem was the distorted perception I had of the people around me. I had a distorted reality. I thought everyone was watching me eat and everyone was waiting to see what size I would be next."

— A Poet and Self-love Warrior

As you complete this chapter, try and determine if any of this information mirrors your child's current behavior. Though we all have maternal instincts, not all of us can identify with every truth, and you may be experiencing different truths regarding your loved one's eating disorder. You might even choose to write those characteristics down for clarity of mind as well as for future reference when you meet with professionals.

If you are just learning about eating disorders and concerned about your child and/or a loved one, this first chapter can feel overwhelming. It is with deep empathy that those of us who have written this book understand how you feel. It can be scary. No matter who you are, how successful, important, famous or not, feeling distraught and uneasy about your child or loved one is a normal human response. For your mental and physical health, you must believe there is hope for full recovery. You must believe you are capable of handling this unwanted situation. You are not alone. Reach out for help, and don't stop inquiring. Our hope is that by reading this book you will began seeing and feeling a sense of oneness/commonality, find a community to help support you, and understand what positive progress looks like. Ultimately, we hope you experience physical and soulful healing as you, your loved one, and your family evolve beyond the eating disorder into a stronger, deeper love for each other and this remarkable life we are blessed with. That day is possible.

Does This Feel Familiar?

"An Eating Disorder? No, Not My child!"

"An eating disorder? I did not even know what an eating disorder was! But what I did know was that my maternal instinct kept loudly yelling, "Something is not right with her. Actually something is terribly wrong! Her lips are blue, why is that? The pediatrician said the erratic behavior, crying, defiant reactions, odd immaturity and withdrawal was just hormonal and this too would pass. She actually commented on Sten's weight loss and how she must have taken good care of herself that summer at camp. 'You look good,' she told Sten. The pediatrician was wrong. It did not pass.

I have lived a colorful life, seen some of the worst the world has to offer and experienced the best. Gifted with wisdom, experience, street smarts, and a strong female psyche, I was afraid of little. But this? This confused me. I did get scared. I was afraid. I could not tap into my own wisdom for answers and my forty-two years of experiences did not offer me any peace. My young daughter, at thirteen years of age, was just as confused as I was. Neither of us had experience with anorexia and neither of us knew the destructive self-loathing force we were about to face!

For two years I lived in a fog of guilt after my child was diagnosed by a specialist with an eating disorder, then she was hospitalized. I constantly questioned myself, wondering how in the world could my child have this problem? No, not my child. I know her better than anyone else on the earth. She's complex but no way could she have a mental disorder! I'm a great mother. What did I do wrong? I have given all of myself to raising children. Our family is good, well respected and resourced. We functioned as a perfectly healthy family. I'm a really loving mom, have a grounded marriage and great kids. How could this have happened? And all of that well "that" was my misguided perspective on how I viewed my healthy life!

Well it did happen and sadly, I lost my confidence those two precious years to self-ridiculing guilt. I was tight-lipped about my daughter's illness because I thought it would protect her from others' judgment. I did not want her to be labeled. I was also hesitant to admit my child's illness so I did not confide in friends or family. I did not want to put this type of pain on my siblings, mom or dad so, I pushed them away, acted strong and thought I could fix my daughter's issues because . . . for God's sake, I am her mom.

I was scared. Scared to death, literally, of losing my child to anorexia, scared of losing my own self and scared of life imploding around me. Internally, I was sad and constantly obsessing. I blamed my husband, I blamed family genetics, I blamed athletics and blamed unprofessional doctors, dieticians and teachers. I was lonely but wrote the loneliness off to being misunderstood. My marriage was almost destroyed and the way I handled my other two children had moments of negative dysfunction. Or should I say, neglected my other daughters and son.

By being secretive about the illness, I was protecting my child's reputation. Or so I thought. Really? Maybe I was worried about my own! I finally realized who the guilt was about. The feelings were real but it was my perspective that kept the guilt alive. The guilt was about me! There was no need to air all our dirty laundry but there was a desperate need to ask for help. Then, finally, I realized there was no shame or weakness in asking for help. So I did. It was at that point the hard work of healing began and I refocused my energy. I asked for help from friends, family and professionals. Just like my child and my family, I too began learning coping skills.

That was twelve years ago. Today, after family counseling and intense honesty, we are comfortable not being a perfect family but being an honest, loving family. With hard honest work our marriage has made it, it is more robust and truth based than before. Yes, we had broken hearts and it hurt like hell, really hurt. But with commitment to honest unconditional love, those fractures mended. And yes, there is scaring but we've learned how to address the past blamelessly and honestly. We were forced to dig deep into our psyche and sincerely lean upon our faith. Our love and respect for one another is far greater than it was a decade ago. Today, we are great together. We know more about who each of us really is and accept the differences all the while working to prop up one another's hopes and dreams. Our daughter, who battled a severe eating disorder for eight years, just graduated college and is living in another state having fun, working full time, being social, interesting, responsible and enjoying a healthy life. There was a moment in time her success was against all odds. But she beat the odds, we beat the odds and we are better people for it. Are we perfect? Absolutely not! There is no perfect. But, we have forgiven each other and we have forgiven ourselves."

— A Once-scared Mother

2

WHAT CAUSES
AN EATING DISORDER?

[
There is a space of intangible measure that has all the answers
we seek. Maybe it's a waste of time to ask "Why?" Maybe we
should proceed with the knowledge and gift of innate human
understanding, learn from what history has taught us, and
proceed with clarity of mind, risk of love, and vulnerable faith.
]

There is a substantial amount of research, both decades old as
well as new, that answers the question: What causes an eating
disorder? And though much of the research is acceptable in defining possible "causes," each case is personal to that individual.

Yet, the most common question we ask ourselves is, *Did I
cause my child's eating disorder?* We have all pondered this painful
question. You are not alone if you feel an odd reflection upon
yourself as a person, your parenting skills, and the guilt of wondering what you did wrong. You are not alone if you consciously
or unconsciously blame yourself for your child's pain. We are
not perfect mothers, and yes, we can intensify and contribute to
our child's problems. (This is one reason we address self-reflection in this book.) But no matter how imperfect you feel, neither
parents nor families cause a child's eating disorder. As listed be-

low, there are variables in life and innate personality traits and environmental factors that contribute to the cause. There are children and adults who have literally experienced hell on earth with lost hope, and yet they do not develop an eating disorder. There are successful, well-resourced, well-educated, loving individuals who fall prey to this unforgiving disease.

You may not have caused it, but we do have the choice of how we treat our children. Your behavior towards your child deeply influences their health and recovery. Intentional or unintentional negative parental behavior does feed their illnesses.

At this point, blame the illness's death grip and know this is not your child's choice. Neither you nor your child intentionally caused the eating disorder. Eating disorders come to fruition through one's own experiences. Two examples we have experienced are traumas and/or a coping crutch.

A trauma can cause the onset of an eating disorder, especially a sexual assault of any kind. Abuse is horrendous and debilitating to any victim, and an eating disorder is often trying to cope with the pain. Less obvious onsets may be when a child has a relative with an eating disorder, is unhealthy regarding weight management, compares themselves to their peers, is a highly sensitive child, or decides to start exercising and dieting and develops an eating disorder as she or he enters puberty. These onsets/causes may be affected by the desire for changed appearance feelings of mastery, power, and superiority.

Initially, a person may choose to control food intake and/or even take extreme measures to reshape her body. In essence, he/she enjoys the control. The orientation of the "cause" may simply begin with weight loss, need for control, and/or the need to feel loved. Before long, no matter the cause, the eating disorder takes control. The disorder affects the mind and then sadly, one's life belongs to the destructive, insidious eating disorder.

They no longer control it; the eating disorder controls her.

There can be variables that are present as the problem develops, which also keep the eating disorder active, and others that predispose individuals for the developing an eating disorder. To further examine the potential causes of an eating disorder, let's discuss different variables.

Genetics

Some individual's inherent gene makeup makes them more susceptible to eating disorders. (Please refer to chapter 3 on genetics in this book.)

Temperament

Temperament is the predisposition to an individual's nature at birth as relating to behavior. Please see the list of common personality traits for people struggling with an eating disorder below.

Predisposition Brain Chemistry

We all have chemical imbalances in the brain's neural pathways. The perfect, ideal human being does not exist. These very human imbalances can cause anxiety, depression, and mental illness. Imbalanced chemicals in the brain can often be regulated with medication. Sadly, there are no stabilizing drugs to combat an eating disorder to date. There are medications for in-tandem illness that accompany eating disorders such as anxiety, compulsion, depression, etc. These can help, but they do not heal the eating disorder. (We recommend you see a licensed eating disorder doctor/psychiatrist to get a valid diagnosis for any type of support drug.)

Psychological Vulnerability

Psychological vulnerability is a susceptible predisposed pattern of thought in one's mind that actually exists before the symptom of an eating disorder materializes. For example, when extreme stress or trauma is encountered, the predisposed vulnerability shapes the individual's response to the problem. For our loved ones the response was an eating disorder.

Biological and Physical Sensation

Ironically, it feels "good" to starve oneself if someone is battling anorexia. Purging (vomiting) is a positive sensation for one struggling with bulimia. There is a release of feel-good chemicals such as dopamine and serotonin.

Environmental Risk Factors

This refers to the characteristics within a person's environment that increases the probability of triggering an eating disorder. Examples of these factors are peer pressure, skewed media exposure of beauty and perfection, dysfunctional family life, being bullied, abuse, stress from school or athletics, and/or having to deal with adult issues at a young age such as death, illness, disaster, etc.

> *"He kept teasing her saying 'You're fat,' and she was only in first grade. Those words affected her psyche and by fourth grade her behavior. He too was just a child. Yes, a bully, but just a child."*
>
> – A Mom

Personality Traits

People with eating disorders share similar personality traits, and some of these traits put a person at greater risk for developing the disorder:

- Perfectionists
- Over-achievers
- Pleasers
- Attention-seekers
- Obsessive-compulsive
- Anxious
- Identity Issues
- Low self-esteem
- Self-critical
- Unhappy with physical appearance
- Sensitive
- Emotional
- Peacemakers
- Highly intelligent
- Routine-oriented
- Persistent
- Emotionally intelligent

Do any of these variables and/or personality traits feel familiar? We can tell you that at times it felt impossible. Can my precious child really feel, experience, and portray these traits? The answer is yes they can. And yet, many of us have grown adult children who have learned to channel their qualities into productive happy lifestyles. No matter how difficult things get and how distant healing feels, know that restoration is possible.

What Could a Mom Do Now?

You may not have the answers you want right now and though pinpointing a cause feels pivotal, please consider the seven suggestions below for the next steps forward.

Stop Obsessing

Because it does get so personal, we as mothers initially get bogged down and lost in the quest of, Why and how did my child get an eating disorder? It is important that we first move forward in getting help for our child rather than obsessing and trying to dissect the causes of our child's illness. Still in a quandary about where your child's eating disorder comes from? Know that you are experiencing a normal process. But initially, it is important to let go of aching over the "whys" and "causes" of your child's disorder. Your questions will potentially be answered in time, especially if and when you engage in therapy, which we highly recommend. It takes time and patience to unravel the complexities of this disease, and eventually the cause(s) and effect(s) will make more sense, though there may not be clear answers.

Stop Blaming

Without a doubt, there are times blame is justified, such as abuse, be it physical, verbal, emotional, or especially as it relates to children.

But there are other times we use "blame" to release our own pain. When we put the blame on others, it relives a burden, and we do not have to look at our own selves. Are you using blame to ease your pain? If so, stop unfairly blaming others and take on the responsibility of learning how to help your child recover. You are wasting your time pointing fingers. We can only say this because some of us did just that, and it was destructive.

"I blamed my husband, but why would I not? It helped to ease my pain! It also was not fair, tore down the trust in our marriage, caused tension in the home and reflected in the children's behavior._Blaming him was a mistake that I wish I could take back. We wasted time that could have been used more constructively. It was not until I saw a therapist that I learned blaming him was an unconscious way of self-navigating my deeps of guilt!"

— A Wife Who Knows That the "Blame Game" Causes Destructive Behavior

Let Go of the Guilt

Guilt has a paralyzing effect, and we moms seem to have an innate issue with guilt! For your child, her/his method of coping with their emotional frustrations came in the form of an eating disorder (rather than drug use, alcoholism, sex, cutting, radical behavior, and/or other physical and emotional outcries) Try your best to move out of a feeling of guilt ("This is my fault"), and keep focused on the other aspects of your child's life that may be keeping the eating disorder alive. Channel your guilt into action and seek out help.

By owning our guilt, we can conquer the feelings of inadequacy and reconstruct our motivation for restoring health in ourselves and our families. If there is a need to apologize, then do so. Guilt disrupts and blocks the potential for a healthy honest relationship with our loved one. We can implode upon ourselves. Go internal; spend time with God and tap into the spiritual place of forgiveness. We teach our kids to love themselves, so we too must love ourselves. Guilt is paralyzing; please find your way of moving beyond it. Ask for forgiveness, and then forgive yourself.

Keep reading and believe there is hope. You will get beyond this state of self-interrogation.

> *"Humbled, broken and weeping, I begged for my child's forgiveness, 'Can you possibly forgive me? Honey, can you please forgive me?' Then my own child, the precious baby I have held and loved for her eighteen years of life took me in her arms and for the first time held me. I remember the strength of her physical embrace as she held on so tight. Very maturely and calmly she said, 'Mom, I forgave you a long time ago.' Then she took my face and looked me in the eyes . . . my little girl with such certainty and clarity said, 'Mom, you have to forgive yourself!' She repeated it over and over. It's the first time I've heard the words. It did not matter how many times I had been granted the out, these same words, I obviously needed it from her. So comfortably with her mother in her arms, she reinforced the truth, 'You are the only one that can forgive yourself Mom.'"*
>
> – A Mom Who Finally Forgave Herself

Keep Focused

Your child needs you. By letting go of the guilt, blame, and obsession, you are able to clear your mind and get focused. And yes, to focus on the issues at hand you will have to prioritize your needs because healing from an eating disorder takes time and effort.

Focus on seeking help and learning how to help your child identify their feelings so that together you can deal with them in a productive way. This means you will have to listen, be patient, and support your child's need to recognize what it is they are feeling. It takes tremendous patience. Stay focused on the coping skills your child needs for healing. Again, we address self-reflection. Are you being open and non-judgmental? Are you focusing on the right things? Focus takes discipline. We cannot do

Please refer to the sections and chapters "Preparing Your Mind," "What's Our Role as Mothers?" and "Self-reflection" in this book.

it right all the time, but it our hope that with your committed focus to solutions you will feel less burdened. Maybe even ask your child what the two of you can focus on together in order to enhance relationships and healing. As mentioned before in this book, when you ask your child's opinions, you should be ready to handle their answers!

Get Off the Rollercoaster

Are you riding alongside your child's emotions, falling prey to their temper, mood, or state of mind? It is almost impossible not to feel our child's fervent intense emotions, and yet, how do we maintain our own stability and rationality? We first begin by getting off their ride.

> *"One of the simplest and best pieces of advice was given to me by my child's psychiatrist, he said, 'GET OFF HER ROLLERCOASTER! You are sitting in the front car with her taking every turn, climbing every hill and plunging down every incline. Get off and stand firmly on the side platform.'"*
>
> — A Mom

Research Professional Help

If you have concluded that your child has a problem, it is time to address professional help. You will need to answer questions such as: With whom do I consult? A pediatrician? Psychologist? Certified eating disorder specialist? Psychiatrist?

> *Please refer to chapter 8, "Get Professional Help For Your Child, Now," and the appendix in this book to help you find the professional help your child, your family, and you need.*

(Please note: We do not recommend diagnosis by a pediatrician but rather a licensed eating-disorder specialist.) Professional help is critical to your child's diagnosis and healing. It's critical to your healing as well!

Excluding many environmental risk factors and psychological vulnerabilities, we as parents have little control over many of the variables in our child's life. We can deliberately tweak, purposefully suggest, and vigorously work to eliminate negative environmental influences, but often we find ourselves at a crossroads trying to deliver an appropriate reaction to environmental variables. We can take our children to medical doctors for drugs and professionals for therapy, and yet, our child's inherent makeup is who they are. Whether they are emotionally intelligent and/or struggle with anxiety, are short-tempered, or sensitive peacemakers, they are our children, and we as mothers will go beyond all reason to help our child.

> *"Your responsibility is to keep her safe and get her to adulthood. She will be an amazing adult!"*
>
> — A Psychiatrist

There is recent neurological research behind potential reasons people develop eating disorders. If you are interested in the details, we recommend Cary Arnold's in-depth book, *Decoding Anorexia*.[4] The information in this book can help you organize your understanding of the biology of eating disorders. Though there is not a "quick cure" for an eating disorder, it is fascinating to read about biological probabilities that cause the disease. Arnold's explanations aid in seeking help, understanding what you are fighting, and our reactions to eating-disordered behavior.

However, beyond scientific variables, there are also the individual variables, personality traits, and defining characteristics of your particular child. What if we took the same traits used by an eating disorder for malicious purpose and used them for good? What if that is our big picture—to empower the attributes? Remember that precious, joyful little child who melted your heart with just a simple smile? The one who danced in the grocery store, who ran full-steam ahead to you in the carpool line, or buried their head in your neck to cry away the day's hurt? The insidious nature of an eating disorder attempts to steal that child away. Sometimes it wins for a while, and you don't recognize the angry, depressed, tortured soul now standing in front of you. That unrecognizable child is someone struggling with an eating disorder. He or she is your loved one, not an "anorexic" and/or "bulimic."

Define Your Child with Positives First!

To the best of your ability, do not let the disease get a leg up on anything. Do not let it define your child. Do not let it define you or your family. You are stronger and far better than this hideous, selfish, life-gripping disease.

---

4. Arnold, Cary. *Decoding Anorexia*. N.p.: n.p., n.d. *Carrie Arnold*. Web. 07 Nov. 2016.

Try to remember and fight for that child, the one who may have inherited personality traits that feel overwhelming at this moment. And remember, it is all parts of this person—however hard they are to rein in—that make up the amazing whole.

When you get angry (and you will), be angry at the disease, not the child. And be angry enough to do something about the situation. Get help from licensed professionals and rediscover that child you know—the one you miss and desire a real relationship with. In doing so, you will also rediscover yourself.

Does This Feel Familiar?

It's Complicated

"My story is complicated. Families are complicated. Eating disorders are complicated! Of the six family members living under our roof, here's what I was dealing with in the spring of 2009: husband (active anorexic), oldest daughter (obsessive compulsive eater), second daughter (active anorexic), son (thin and in need of gaining weight), third daughter (confused), and me (scared, lonely, pissed off, and frustrated). You just cannot imagine meals at our house. They were impossible to prepare, serve, or sit through. The stares, comments, and emotions . . . you could cut those with a knife. I watched cautiously, as my second daughter became healthier and unhealthier at the same time. She became very careful about everything that she ate and was only eating "healthy" foods. At the same time, she was becoming more and more withdrawn from me and from her peers. There was clearly a separation, distancing going on. She did not want to be seen, discovered. She didn't want the world to see that everything was not perfect, so she tried extra hard to make it look perfect. It was terrifying to watch a beautiful and brilliant young girl starve herself in order to be more beautiful and more loved. This child could achieve anything she put her mind to and being thin was what she was focused on. At the very same

time, my first daughter was struggling in school, socially, and emotionally, and she soothed herself with food. Food was her friend, her lover, her medication, and her entertainment. She was becoming and would become morbidly obese. She was always hungry and completely insatiable. She could not fill the void in her belly that was loneliness and shame with enough food. This was also terrifying. Some of the disordered eating issues at our house are still works in progress, but this story is about the journey, particularly mine. Along my journey to "help my children"—because I thought I could—I found a young Ph.D. who specialized in eating disorders. She told me about a program/curriculum she had written for a group of young girls who were struggling with different issues surrounding their worthiness—eating disorders included. I was intrigued, so I invited her to do this program with eleven of my friends and me. We went on a three-day retreat where we intensely did a program called Embody Love Workshop. Listen when I tell you that I (we) wept and wept. It was a transformational experience.

During and after this experience, I realized that I still cared about my external appearance and believed that it was relative to some extent to my worthiness! It was a total reality check that sent me completely over the edge. What part of me had contributed to the complete dysfunction going on in my very own home? I immediately got a therapist and did some very intense self-reflection. I realized that spending time and energy focusing on what I looked like was a giant waste of time and was detrimental to my family members and all who I was in relationship with. How I feel about myself lives outside of me and impacts the people around me. I was already beautiful and an amazing human being and mother. I shifted my perspective completely. I was moving on . . .

Next on the agenda was making sure that other girls and women could realize that their worthiness has nothing to do with their external appearance and that nothing needs to change about them in order for them to be loved. We all have unique gifts and talents to offer the world, but we cannot realize them if we are focused on what doesn't matter about us. I began offering workshops as prevention of eating disorders, low self-esteem, substance abuse, sexual *violence, and suicide. Organically, two of my daughters became involved in this work and have inspired many girls and women to focus on their inner beauty and celebrate who they are. Working together to prevent eating disorders and inspire others has been a very healing activity for our family. Even my son has benefited from the work we are doing. We have a lot of conversations about what is "beautiful," particularly surrounding girls and women. Do I have regrets? No. We live in a culture where thinness and dieting is celebrated. Perspective is skewed, and body shaming is acceptable and ingrained in our language, both verbally and non-verbally. I was doing my best. My heart was in the right place, but my mind got distracted. During the healing process, several members of my family and I were trying to realign our lives and be in integrity with food, exercise, purpose, and each other. In reflection, I have a few recommendations to mothers whose eyes, ears, and hearts are open to hearing them—women who are committed to the healing process even if it means having to look deeply and courageously in the mirror at themselves.*

- *Act! Do not react. Confront your daughter with your truth. What you see and think is dangerous for your daughter is real. Do not be afraid of her reaction. You are saving her life. Even if you think she is just "dappling" in weight loss, have your daughter explore why this is important to her.*
- *Network and get the help you need! Talk to friends and family and seek the best help possible for your child. Friends and family are your best resource and support system. Once you have a support system in place for your child, set one up for yourself. You cannot do this alone.*
- *Stay vigilant: I believe that anorexia and bulimia are addictions, and addicts are master manipulators. They work very hard to get where they are in their disease and will not easily let go of it. Stick with the plan/boundaries you have set up with your support system. My second daughter talked me into treatment that was the least invasive into her life and the most private. I deeply regret this decision. She manipulated me (again). We were both motivated by fear, afraid*

that the "interruption" would be harmful to her GPA and college application process.

- *Treat the disorder! Life cannot and will not go on until you do. Intensive treatment is imperative. Patients need 100 percent accountability. An eating disorder is a disease and needs to be treated as such. I finally got my first daughter into a treatment center last year and wish I had done so sooner. These disorders become embedded in the psyche. Don't wait to seek help[5]!*

- *Surrender! This does not mean give up. Ultimately, you are powerless to help your child unless they help themselves. Let them work within the perimeters you have set up to find what works for them. They will have to figure this out, and the coping skills they learn will be theirs for life. You must surrender and trust God and the process. When we obsess over their wellbeing, we forget about our own. We matter. We have families that are counting on us. We must be clear about what is healthy for us so we can set good boundaries and examples for our children and the world. Be kind, patient, and compassionate with yourself during this process and forever.*

- *Finally, if we believe in God—and I do—then we believe that we are all born beautifully, imperfectly, and for a purpose that only we can fulfill. Help your children see the beauty within themselves— their characteristics, talents, and passions—by seeing it in yourself first. Self-care is loving and helpful to the entire family. Choose self-love, so your children can too."'*

— A Mom Who Believes Everyone is Born Worthy

5. "Eating Disorder Predisposition Is Associated with ESRRA and HDAC4 Mutations." *National Center for Biotechnology Information.* U.S. National Library of Medicine, n.d. Web. 07 Nov. 2016.

3 IS AN EATING DISORDER GENETIC?

[
Genetics + Temperament + Intense Emotional Intelligence +
Risk Factors = Manifestation of an Eating Disorder
]

To answer this question, "Is an eating disorder genetic?" let us examine the combination of genetics, temperament, intense emotional intelligence, and risk factors.

Genetics

Interestingly enough, there is research suggesting that our inherent gene makeup can be a large contributor to the cause of an eating disorder. But what does that really mean? We have found similarities amongst our loved ones and friends with eating disorders, and thus a pre-disposed genetic makeup is reasonable. No doubt, eating disorders are more common when a first-degree family member has a history of eating disorders, a genetic tie. Most of us are exposed to the media's false interpretation of beauty, body image, and success, and yet, less than 1 percent of our population is affected by anorexia. The case for genetic predisposition is heavily favored. For some people eating disorders are a deep-seeded genetic intersection, and for others it is circumstance.

The research concerning genetics and eating disorders is on the forefront of the medical frontier. For example, there is research on the mutation of genes tied to

> *For more information on medical research and the ESRRA and HDAC4 gene study, please refer to the appendix in this book.*

eating disorders such as the combination of the ESRRA and HDAC4 genes. Our hope is that before too long, scientists and doctors will be able to pinpoint a genetic combination and thus find a suitable cure.[6]

One of the most fascinating aspects of biology and eating disorders is the neuroplasticity of the brain and its link to eating disorders. Neuroplasticity is the ability of the brain to change, meaning the brain has the ability to rewire itself allowing the creation of new behaviors or the rewiring of old behaviors i.e. eating-disorder behavior. Scientists no longer believe our brains are hard-wired from childhood to death; to the contrary, the brain can encounter changes by repetitive mental experiences. Experiences and behavior actually create neuroplasticity and brain structure

> *For more information on neuroplasticity and eating disorders, please refer to the appendix in the back of the book.*

change. Behavioral therapy for eating disorders is seen as a positive probability of rewiring eating-disorder behavior. Change the behavior repetitively, and the brain will change. There are no psychotic drugs to cure eating disorders, but the probability of rewiring negative eating disorder thoughts is hopeful.[7]

6. Uiowa. "Two Genes Linked to Increased Risk for Eating Disorders." Iowa Now. N.p., 19 Mar. 2015. Web. 07 Nov. 2016. www.now.uiowa.edu/2013/10/two-genes-linked-increased-risk-eating-disorders

7. By Repeatedly Practicing Healthy Behaviors, We Will Become Healthier. "The Neuroplasticity of the Brain." The Emily Program. N.p., n.d. Web. 07 Nov. 2016. www.emilyprogram.com/blog/the-neuroplasticity-of-the-brain.

Temperament

We are born with an inherent nature that affects our way of living life, and it is different for every single human being. Temperament is wildly complex and absolutely unique for everyone. The inherent individual temperament can set the stage for an eating disorder to manifest. Similar temperament characteristics are seen in those who struggle with eating disorders. For example:

- Anxiety
- Intensity
- Sensitivity
- Perfectionism
- People-pleasing
- High intelligence/IQ
- High emotions
- Tender-heartedness
- Social dependency
- Ambition/Over-achievement
- Routine-oriented
- Persistence
- Emotional Intelligence/EQ

Intense Emotional Intelligences (EI/EQ)

EI, also referred to as emotional quotient, is about self-awareness and awareness of those around you. Emotionally Intelligent people have the capacity to recognize their own emotions with an understanding of self and also perceive the emotions of others. EI discriminates between the different feelings, recognizing how they affect those around you. It also involves perception of other people and how you think they perceive you. This information is then used to guide behavior and thinking.

EI is often seen in individuals struggling with an eating disorder. Before the brain is fully developed, Emotional Intelligence can cause havoc on one's ability to identify, use, understand, and manage emotions within one's self and the ability to read and react to emotions in others. Everything feels like it is on overdrive and dramatic. EQ can be seen as a problem, but when channeled positively and with maturity, it can be beneficial. Once identified, it would be constructive to support your child's ability to manage emotions in positive ways to relieve stress, communicate effectively, empathize with others, overcome challenges, defuse conflict, problem-solve, and learn to adapt these characteristics when dealing with others. Emotional Intelligence impacts many different aspects of one's daily life, most especially behavior and relational interaction. Most of us involved in writing this book have noticed these characteristics in our children since childhood. An Emotionally Intelligent child is often more challenging to raise, but when matured, they make the most awesome, sound, and well-rounded adults. Is your child Emotionally Intelligent?

Risk Factors

Risk factors vary but can be attributed to the structure of the culture one lives within, history of childhood, family history, traumas encountered, transitions and change, low self-esteem (learned or innate), involvement in competitive sports, work, artistic activities, gender, and/or a combination of humanity's influences. Along with the biological influence, exposure to Western culture's obsession with beauty, society's depiction of thin, the distorted media, false success, situational stress, mishaps, and copious lifestyles make our children more susceptible to developing an eating disorder. (Review chapter 2.)

"Comparison can be an ugly thing. As an identical twin, the world always compares you. Even as a sibling, the world compares you. Your identity can easily be either enmeshed with your twin or based off a scale of comparison you measure against your twin. You have to truly develop a new mantra in terms of who you are. Rather than 'the more athletic one," "the more artistic one," the thinner one," the "one with the cowlick," you must train yourself to turn off that voice and look inside to who you really are. One can easily blame this challenge as a cause or a feeling of unworthiness or slight."

– A Twin Who Lost Her Sister to Anorexia

What Could a Mom Do Now?

The origin of genetics for your child is imprinted beyond just you and his or her father. Genetics are developed from generations past—both the paternal and maternal sides. That's a bundle of genetics! Below are four ideas to consider.

Recognize Initially This is Not Your Child's Choice

Your child did not choose this disease even if it began by dieting or desired weight loss. Even in the most frustrating of times, step back and remember this is not the choice our children would prefer. Remember to fight the disease, not the child. In order to fight effectively we have to know the enemy. Educating yourself with the information in this book is a great start. Your child will remember feelings of affection and love but not all details from the depth of illness. No child would choose the type of pain an eating disorder causes.

> *"I remember in specific when I would cry and get over-whelmed, my parents didn't condemn me for struggling, but they hugged me, told me it was okay to feel what I was feeling, and that they believed in me. My mom became a very safe place for me, where I could confess if I had been deceptive, if I had lied about my food, and where I could just cry and be held. Now, ten years later, that season of my life remains very blurry. Whether the fogginess is a side effect of my actual brain and body being so unhealthy or it's protection from difficult memories, it's pretty blurry."*
>
> – Now a Healthy and Happily Married Woman

Work Preventatively

In the book, *The Parent's Guide to Eating Disorders,*[8] prevention is discussed as a means to reducing risk, highlighting different efforts used in arming your child both emotionally and socially. The authors, Marcia Herrin, EdD, MPH, RD, and Nancy Matsumoto, attempt to teach parents how to provide warmth, attention, affection, and empathy as they strive for a close meaningful relationship with their child. It sounds like natural behavior, but for some parents and other caregivers it must be learned. It is important to take the time necessary to learn both verbal and physical communication skills. We can work preventatively by nurturing our children's self-esteem and help develop a secure and healthy outlook on body image. In early child development, tighten the

---

8. Herrin Marcia Herrin Ed.D. M.P.H. R.D. (Author),, Marcia, and Nancy Matsumoto. *Parent's Guide to Eating Disorders: Supporting Self-Esteem, Healthy Eating, and Positive Body Image at Home* Paperback – July 28, 2007.

boundaries on your child's environment and their exposure to the culture's toxic attitude towards unrealistic beauty and body shape. Our child's attitude towards physical beauty and a healthy body image begins with us.

> *"My anorexia started the summer between my sophomore and junior year of high school. I was at a vulnerable position that summer, having broken up with my boyfriend of two-and-a-half years, and taken on a very stressful academic and extracurricular load. In truth, the roots of it were there much earlier. As a child, I watched my mom struggle with diet after diet. When I was ten, I can remember drinking diet shakes to be like her. Of course, at that age, I also chased that with a cheeseburger. But, the message was there: women struggle with food, with weight, with body image, and somehow this is all tied up in the core of who we are, how we perceive ourselves, how others perceive us."*
>
> – Now a Mother of Two, Redefining Body Image

Interpreting Help

It is important to focus on what you can do to help your child with healing. It is also important to recognize that there are times you cannot help your loved one in the healing process, most especially for older teens and adult children. There is a fine line to decipher when our parental behavior is enabling versus empowering. No doubt, your child will have to make some defining decisions, and honestly, you cannot make those decisions for them. You can help with decision-making, but eventually it is up to your loved one battling the eating disorder to make a change. As an adult, this recognition of reality takes time and patience because we want to fix the problem.

Ask the professionals you choose to help your child, your family, and yourself.

> *"I would like you to discuss a plan that launches these kids into the world as they prepare to deal. Once we feel they are ready, how do we help move them into the world with new insight . . . an insight free of an eating disorder? I'm talking in a physical sense as well. Move them out from under our wing and teach them to fly on their own. This is what our seventeen-year-old daughter is currently learning. Just like it is difficult for your patients to leave you, imagine how scary it might be to leave a safe sanctuary if not prepared."*
> – An Email to a Therapist from a Mom in Need

Self-reflection

When looking at genetics and environmental factors, we must also look at our own behavior. All of us moms should take a good look at ourselves and the inventory of our strengths and shortcomings regarding the ways in which we model self-love and acceptance. Our children watch us closely and model our behavior.

> *"Be it subconscious or with full awareness, I want you to know, Mom, that I am affected by the example you set for me, I think it started from the moment I first opened my eyes."*
> – From a Twenty-Year-Old Daughter in Recovery

Over the years and on several occasions, the women writing this book have all had to look into our own mirrors and, at times, make changes. We've had to seek personal help from therapists and counselors. Sometimes it was difficult to see fallibility, yet we are grateful and better for the work. No mother is perfect. Our own genetic makeup is not perfect. Not you, not me—not one of us is, or will be, perfect! That's the beauty of being human, and that is perfectly exquisite! Guilt-free, ask yourself a few self-reflective questions:

- How does my child see me as a woman?
- Do I portray positive body image?
- Do I mind my words?
  - Don't ever call your child fat or pudgy.
  - Don't comment on other people's bodies.
  - Don't compare your child to others.
- Do I champion the false images the media paints, or am I too seduced by the fiction?
- Am I trying to be the "perfect" mom, or do I accept my mistakes all the while loving my child and admitting my human shortcomings?
- Are my expectations reasonable both for my child and for myself?
- Do I allow for vulnerability in others and within myself?
- Do I listen and discuss issues firmly but thoughtfully? Do I really listen to what my child is saying?
- Am I asking my child to be part of my plan, or am I trying to understand their own?
- Do I nurture my child's self-esteem?
- Do I help my child see his or her strengths? Do I discuss their strengths positively?
- How do I cultivate self-worth and self-respect for my

child and myself?

- If I have had or do have my own eating disorder, am I working for my own recovery?
- Much of the way we view life is a choice. Am I making a choice to rejoice in the positives or dwell in the negatives? Positives and negatives always co-exist.

It would be of great value if you and your child could have a conversation answering the above questions together. You may consider working with a therapist if you feel uneasy asking these questions and having a conversation with your loved one.

You should be mentally and emotionally prepared for these discussions as there may be uncomfortable responses from your child. When they answer honestly, you don't want to overreact. Honest exchange can be worthwhile, but hateful arguments are harmful. You as the adult must be steady and ready. We have learned that staying grounded in your parental role is essential, power struggles and control-freak issues between a mom and a child struggling with an eating disorder are destructive, nurturing a child's self-worth is imperative, and fighting the disease versus the child is critical.

> *For further information on professional help, please refer to the chapter "Get Professional Help for Yourself, Now."*

This conversation about self-reflection is important and personal. Take a step back and look at yourself objectively. What are your motives? Why do you (or don't you) respond the way you do? How will you know if you are not brutally honest with yourself?

> *For more detail, please refer to chapter 6 "Self-reflection" in the book.*

Does This Feel Familiar?

My Wish is That You Grow Up Loving Yourself

Dear Darling Daughter,

That's what my mom called me, her darling daughter. I have different pet names for you, my sweet three-year-old, but the one my mom had for me is still close to my heart. I am writing this to you today, but will not ask you to read it until you are much older. This is a story about me and my mother, about you and me and about all women who need to learn the valuable lesson of valuing themselves.

My mom loved me more than anything, just as I love you more than anything. Sadly, my mom did not always love herself. She did not have very high self-esteem. She struggled with her body image and her weight. She was overweight even as a very young child and never outgrew it. She was on diets as long as I knew her. Even though she was one of the sweetest, most beautiful people you could ever imagine, she did not always think highly of herself. She put everyone else first. More often than not, she did not meet her own needs. She was an amazing caregiver and mother, wife, friend and teacher. Everyone who knew her was lucky to have her as part of her life. I just wish she had realized more clearly how incredible she was and had been a little more selfish with her own self-care.

I never doubted how much my mom loved me. She was my best friend. I hurt her very deeply when I decided during high school to stop eating. I had always been a very thin and active child, played lots of sports and never had trouble with my weight. Then at the beginning of high school I began to get "rounder" and wanted to stay very thin. I started to restrict what I ate, and exercise more and more. Finally, one day I was hardly eating anything and was exercising twice a day. I looked like a skeleton. My mom confronted me and said, "I know you are doing this because you don't want to look like me." "That's not true," I said. But it was partially true. Even truer was that I didn't want to lose control of my body and felt a need to have greater control in my life. In an effort to maintain control, I completely lost myself. I lost my self-esteem. I lost my personality. I withdrew from my friends and family. My plan to be perfect and look perfect backfired. I lost sight of what was important in life—my own self-worth. I was worth more than skin and bones. If I had loved myself, I would not have starved myself. If I could have seen my own value and beauty, I wouldn't have tried so hard to give myself more value and beauty by seeking an unattainable "thin and attractive" body.

For you, my dear, I wish that you will grow up loving yourself. I hope you will take the time and energy to meet your own needs. Feed yourself nourishing food. Get healthy amounts of exercise. But even more importantly, speak words of kindness and support to yourself. In the end, as much as mothers try to help and love and support their daughters, you will need to be your own best friend, your own support and your own cheerleader. When the stresses of school, work, relationships, marriage, babies and friendships get you down, you will need to call on your own inner reserves age to sustain yourself and tell yourself that YOU ARE WORTH IT. You are worth spending the time caring for yourself. Find things you enjoy and practice them. Realize that you are beautiful inside and out, no matter what shape or size you are. I hope I live a long, long time and can tell you these things myself. My mother told me those things all the time. But I think if she had told them to herself, that would have been much more powerful.

For you, my girl, I am going to love myself every day. I'm going to tell myself that I am beautiful and strong. I'm going to exercise and eat and grow and learn. I'm going to take time for myself when I need it because I deserve it. I'm going to enjoy dressing up in clothes to go on dates with your father no matter what size I am. I'm going to have fun swimming and playing with you even if I'm not the thinnest mom at the pool or on the beach. I'm going to keep up my own hobbies and try to do things that bring me joy so I can show you what that looks like. I'm going to work hard and use my gifts and talents in my craft. I'm going to tell you very clearly that I love myself and that I AM WORTH IT. That will be my greatest lesson for you.

All my love from the very bottom of my heart,
Mom

NOTES

NOTES

NOTES

NOTES

WHAT'S OUR ROLE AS CARETAKERS?

"Will I be enough to love, to want back? Am I worthy of affection because I can't find anywhere that says I am. All I want is to belong, to be validated . . . I'm not simply damned. Because here is my struggle day in and day out. One way or another I will not be enough for someone else. Because I am lost in the self-obsession of my own mind. Getting high off of self-abuse, hatred, and crime. But it is an issue you see because the intoxication begins and ends with me. I am not enough. I am unworthy. I am not loveable. I am not beautiful. I am too much to handle . . . too sensitive, too emotional, too dramatic."

– Diary of a Teen in the Depths of an Eating Disorder

4 PREPARING YOUR MIND

[
Preparing your mind in advance of the potential storms
seems critical to one's sanity.
]

Now that we've discussed what an eating disorder is, the potential causes, the effects of genetics, and debilitating affects this illness has on the brain, it is time to prepare yourself mentally for what is to come. This is potentially a five-to-ten-year journey with your loved one, and that can feel scary. We often become paralyzed by the fear of losing our child to this disease. You will experience loneliness and isolation at times. It can feel overwhelming, and there are moments you'll feel your world crashing in. It's imperative that you do your best to stay strong in mind, soul, and body. We are responsible for our own happiness and stability.

Mothers must believe that they have an important role in their child's recovery and then own the responsibility as the parent. Parents are potentially the most influential force in their child's life. Parent(s) + child(ren) = family. However that looks in your life, it is impactful. There are effects and consequences to all family units because your child's interaction within the family helps them develop an identity. Family members feel the effect and consequences of each other's actions. Each member has a role within the family, and if one struggles, the rest of the family feels that pain. Similar to wind chimes, when one is broken, the harmony declines. This disease affects the whole family.

By birthright or choice your child is exactly that: your child. You are the mother, not your child's friend and not one of your child's peers. Recognizing your pivotal role as a guardian on behalf of your child's illness in a supportive way is extremely important. Consider yourself a resource and an advocate for your child. Just as important, take care of your physical and mental health. Yes, you are the mother but not a god and not Superwoman. Ask for help!

Below we have listed pro-active suggestions to build your mental pillars of overall health and answer questions such as: How do I keep myself grounded, stable, and able? Who is in my support network? Of course, you cannot implement all these suggestions immediately, you may not fit within all the categories below, and you will have additional ideas, thoughts, and opinions that pertain to your life.

What Could a Mom Do Now?

Listen to Your Intuition

A woman's intuition is as powerful as the unwritten oath of motherhood. It acts as an internal guide urging you to do, to sense, and to react. It is always present, yet we sometimes ignore this innate gift. We may not always read "our gut" correctly, and sometimes we second-guess ourselves. Remember, the gift of maternal intuition is ever-present no matter how deeply buried within your soul. Listen to your intuition and motivate yourself to react when you "know" something is just not right with your child. A mother knows when her child is in distress. Try to find the words to explain what your gut is telling you, share your feelings, and seek proactive advice from a doctor, a friend, a family member, or a trusted kindred spirit. Remember, the mind can lie, but the gut cannot!

> *"I did not know how much vertical depth I was capable of. I knew other strong women but if you told me that I would move beyond my current capacity . . . well, I would question your opinion. I was already experienced, well-versed in life and strong. But what I did not know was that my own daughter would become my "Window to the World" and to myself. I was capable of digging deeper."*
>
> – A Mom

Prioritize

When caregiving a child with an eating disorder, we recommend that you prioritize your life. Simplify. Make an agreement with yourself (between you and God and/or with a person who keeps you accountable) to settle into the journey. Streamline by letting go of frivolous activities, learning to say no, and respecting your personal boundaries. Take a look at your life's priorities and decide what you can do away with and remold now, before this relentless disease takes you into an abyss. (For more suggestions, please refer to chapter 5, "Streamline Your Life.")

No doubt you will make mistakes. Be considerate of yourself and preset those safety nets! You will not regret your efforts, but you will regret not focusing on your child's recovery with intention, vigor, patience, and love. It's not easy, but parenting a child will potentially be your most important life's work!

Educate Yourself

If you suspect that your child has an eating disorder or is in recovery from an eating disorder, continue to educate yourself by reading. This book is written modularly, so skip if you choose and review chapters when necessary.

Nurture Your Family

When one person in a family has an eating disorder, everyone suffers. Mothers often feel like the cornerstone to the emotional health of a family and are concerned with questions like, How do I deal with the intense emotional states this is building in my family? Undeniably, it is a challenge. We have discussed the need to prioritize, educate yourself, and listen to your intuition, but how do we nurture the other children who do not have an eating disorder? Begin by making them feel safe, be non-confrontational, speak lovingly, spend intentional quality time together, physically hold and touch them, put them to bed at night, try to be there when they wake, be honest, and ask them to be patient during this unsettling time. Try your best to continue the behaviors, endeavors, or activities that are special between you and each of your children. Children need reassurance. Make sure they know you love them equally and the attention on the child struggling is not favoritism. Sadly, it is often the siblings who go unnoticed because we are hyper-focused on the ill child. You will find yourself spending an inordinate amount of time, energy, and mental anguish dealing with the one member who has the eating disorder. The great dichotomy is tending to your healthy children while responsibly supporting the recovery of the one afflicted child. Remember, neither you, the ill child, or your other children are at fault. They simply want love and at-tention, but you have a child being strangled by an eating dis-order.

From the Other Side

"I am a sister of someone who struggled with anorexia for ten years. In many cases, certainly in my life, the siblings can be overshadowed by the victim's disease. As a family member closely bound to my once victimized sister, I am here to tell you what it is like from my side of the story.

I too struggled hand in hand with my sister's eating disorder. Although I did not have anorexia, her eating disorder placed a burden upon my childhood because it affected every-one in our lives not just her. I can tell you from the bottom of my heart, whether you're a sister or a mother, there are many days, weeks even months that you feel like giving up. But, when we dare to love, we can't forget that we allow ourselves to be engulfed by this powerful emotion. We are agreeing to be there through thick and thin. "Till death do us part" is how I like to put it, and for my family that is oh so true.

You as a mother, much like my mom, are seen as the caretaker. When your children are in trouble or need, you are looked at to come to the rescue. Now, although the eat-ing disorder may seem the most important thing at the time, it is really the whole family who deserves to win.

Anorexia has a tendency to skew our views as to what is important at the time, leading the eating disorder to be the main focus. Yes, healing your sick child and giving them the focus they need is crucial, however, the effect this illness places on the ones that love the victim are crippling. Me, now a child of eighteen, who watched my sister struggle for a decade, can tell you moms that we need you to watch us too. Balance is my advice for you. Largely because eating disorders demand attention, and it's hard for us to watch someone we love suffer while we drown in our own loneliness. Talk to us, tell us enough to alleviate our fears, even if we don't really understand everything. I needed to believe my sister was going to be okay.

"So, as a mother who wants the best for their children, love the sick and as purposefully, love the healthy. We need your love just as much as some stupid eating disorder that wants to take the love away from all of us."

— A Sister

We have found that supportive spouses, friends, and family members can and will come to your rescue. You have to ask for help. This is critical: Ask for help. You cannot do it all, and others are capable of helping. If you have a spouse who is a loving father/partner, lean on them for help with the children. The children belong to them as well. Good family counseling will benefit everyone.

You will be angry, and if you are not educated and understand this disease, you will mistakenly be mad at the child. Anger, impatience, and frustration are normal reactions.

"My first reaction was to be mad at her, and I was for a long time. After all, her behavior re-oriented the dynamic

of her family, propelling them down an exhausting path of anguish and frustration. She seemed indifferent to the sometimes excruciating angst her family was experiencing (especially her mom and dad). It was hard to understand how a teenager with an eating disorder could seemingly become the self-centered, disruptive gravity point of the family . . . It was hard to understand until years later, after she (with the irreplaceable help of faith, family and professionals) fought her way out of the disease. It was hard to understand until I realized she battled a disease, not a choice. It was hard to understand until I saw my sister advocating for her daughter and fighting alongside of her every day. It was hard to understand until I saw the aftermath of the struggle—a healthier family than it would have been without the pain. A family whose individuals are now anchored by deeply bonded, abiding, and loving relationships."

— An Uncle Who Finally Understood

Build Your Village of Support

Do any of your friends or family members have experience with eating disorders? Go talk to them and get educated on how they chose to deal with the issue. You may choose differently, but the education is worth it. Be bold and ask them for advice, referrals, and knowledge. In the early stages it is easy to doubt yourself and your choices. Are they right? Am I wrong?

This is not about who is right or wrong; it's about getting the necessary support from others to help strengthen your foundation. Ask for help, accept help, be thankful for the help, and believe there will be a day you will give back to others.

My Dear Friend

"Thank you for sharing your worries and fears with me yesterday. Thank you for trusting me. I empathetically hold you close at heart, share your maternal pain and will continue to look for the light in her recovery. In the most difficult of times there is often unpredictable answers. Like the dark side of life we cannot see but when reveled it feels obvious. I pray, optimistically, that a constructive purpose will emerge from this difficult time that, for you, must feel like hell.

I heard the fear in your voice, the torment of assuming and wondering what the future has to bear. I can only speak from the experience as a mother but want you to know that I, and millions of other mothers, know that feeling of being overcome with fear. Not fear for our own selves but distress and angst on behalf of our child. No matter how strong we are perceived to be, the skillful roles we perform in life, our accomplishments, and/or our significance as a woman, when we see our own children in pain we are momentarily incapacitated and paralyzed in the fear. We have immense fear of losing them and fear of what they have to personally face.

So if you don't mind, I want to share a few personal thoughts that were once shared with me in a desperate time of need. As you know, we too have dealt with a child's psychotic break and no doubt, it is horrifically scary. Don't know if it makes you feel any better but please know that you're not alone. We have seen so many teenagers literally crater as their world implodes around them. Professional help, unconditional love and medication, if necessary, seem to be the best medicine.

Be prepared to listen. It takes lots of patience to listen as well as allowing them space to personally process. No matter if you are totally freaked out internally, do your best to keep a calm external. We think we are prepared to hear anything but . . . "anything" can be shocking! A traumatic experience can trigger psychosis so let's pray there is no abuse, witness to something beyond reason or harm in anyway. But if there is, there is a harsh reality that we cannot go backwards in time so what is real is real. I know you will gracefully handle whatever comes your way and that does not mean with our worry, stress or mistakes. You have already dealt head-on with extremes in life. This too, whatever it may be, you will once again handle gracefully. You always have and you always will.

Do your best to respond without judgment, you are a master at this and have shared your non-judgmental philosophies with me always. Many years ago I was told to, "mind your tone, mind your words, mind your body language and remember to empower her without judgment. All the while . . . create a comfortable loving home, give attention to other loved ones, work to get out of the obsessive thoughts, maintain your individuality and put your creativity on paper to eventually share with others!" I remember looking to my mentor friend feeling speechless with a "UMMMM Hmmmm! I did not do it all well at first but with time was able to balance most of it. Certainly not without flaws. You will be wonderful my friend, you had amazing teachers (still have your mom) and not only are you well-versed, you are well-trained She is lucky to have you as a mother. She will desperately need you and your husband at her side. If she says she feels unsafe there is probably a reason for that. Thank God she has you and her Dad as her safety nets.

Hug her, touch her, kiss her forehead and open up the physical boundaries to let her be your child. They try to be so grown up and sometimes what they need the most is the reassurance of unconditional love and comfort.

There is no shame in mental illness, there is no shame in emotional disorders. It's a part of who we are and often greatness comes from those minds. There is no shame. Discernment? Yes, but not shame. We should all remember never to use words that shame our loved in a crisis. Once stable, she will have a long road ahead of her as she processes the past events and often shame is a tormenting component. I learned that from a professional and then had to learn how to implement that into my verbiage. Being a millennial kid, she will find a way to gift back to the world with what she knows. Sometimes it is us moms who feel the pain and anguish long after they have moved on.

All things are reconcilable, not always as we planned, but reconcilable nonetheless. There is no normal, there is just life. And with that comes the perfectly imperfect!

I love you dearly and am here for you always, just like you have been for me."

— From One Mom to Another

You do not need to reinvent the wheel; most likely there are others who have been where you are and/or are currently in the same position as you. Surround yourself with a community of caring individuals who will encourage you rather than interrogate or judge you and thereby deepen the wound. A true friend, loving spouse, and reliable family member who is honest can be very helpful. Listen to their constructive criticism! It all depends on the motive. So, find the people whose motive is to include, understand, support, and love you through this trying time. Make phone calls to "those" people, and do not procrastinate. A lonely idle mind does not serve you well! Set a timely goal for yourself to call a friend, set up a therapy session, see your girlfriends, have a date night with your mate, visit your mentor, your family, your priest, and/or whoever you need in your village. A mom needs to find appropriate time to talk about the challenging issues. It feels most healthy when we can balance compulsive talk and personal internalization. You need your friends, and you need to talk! Human beings are not created to live alone. We thrive most successfully together. We have always lived, worked, and played in "villages"—it is up to you to reach out and find that community.

> *"I lived three very lonely years because I was afraid to ask for help. I lost productive time as my child continued to get sicker and sicker. I know now it was a mistake to keep the pain to myself. It actually caused my child more pain."*
> – A Mom Who Was Lonely

Get Centered in Your Faith

We live in both the physical realm of life as well as the spiritual realm. Call it what you may, but there exists both the tangible physical body and the mysterious soul within the physical human body. Recovering from an eating disorder and/or caretaking a loved one battling is most successful when we nurture both realms of life. Ultimately, love is the comprehensive answer. (Please refer to the chapter "Faith Practices" in this book.)

> *"If we are not able to love ourselves well, we will have a hard time loving God and others. Loving ourselves is an immediate cure that is either the start of faith or the beginning of a new chapter in faith. After all, we are created in a divine image."*
>
> — A Nineteen-Year-Old Boy

If you currently practice a faith that works for you, we recommend you continue. If not, perhaps it's time to seek out the Divine. A relationship with the Divine can help alleviate stress and manage uncertainties.

> *"I turn my worries over and pray every morning for God's angels to guide and protect my children. I thank God every night for one more day that I was not lost in fear and worry."*
>
> — A Mom of Many

Healthy Physical Exercise

If you are involved in a healthy exercise program, continue. Exercise helps with stress management, boosts brainpower, clarity of mind, and cognitive functions, and can aid in revoking depression. Moving the body also inhibits an idle mind and obsessive thought! But be aware—when you exercise, your child will watch your every move! Your physical activities can be triggering for a child whose exercise had been reduced or stopped by their doctor and/or treatment team. So if that's the case, do not exercise in front of them. Also, be aware that your child hears your words, so stop constantly talking about your exercise programs, your weight, your body, and/or the latest diet craze. Responsibly evaluate your exercise habits. Do they impair your family time or personal relationships? Is it healthy or compulsive? Are you teaching your child a positive attitude toward exercise?

Take up or continue yoga, a team sport, exercise class, dance class, running, hiking, biking, jogging, walking, and/or any type of exercise you enjoy. Be accountable with your exercise regimen and be respectful of your child' perspective regarding your regimen.

We recommend yoga for overall health of body, heart, and mind.

Engage in Life

During this challenging time of life, try your best not to lose yourself to despair and worry. This is a common problem for parents and easier said than done. Lighten up when appropriate. Engage your "village" and go do something fun outside of the eating disorder world. Go see a movie, have a picnic outside, take a long walk, listen to live music, enjoy a date night, go to an event, spend time with adult friends, visit a museum, get outside of the home environment, travel if appropriate, continue your art form, join a book club, go to your place of worship, share a meal with friends, and partake in activities that stimulate you mentally. You need to seek out joy and feel like a whole being, not just the mother of a child with an eating disorder. Get the family out and get out of the rut by engaging in your own life and in the lives of others. The way you choose to live your life is an example to your family.

Visualization

Visualization is an easy and healing practice. Close your eyes, go internal, and picture your child healthy and happy. See your child healthy. View your child healthy. Visualize your child healthy in your mind's eye. Your brain simulates visualization, and a reality of that vision can be manifested. Imagery is habitual. For example, we often ask, "Do you see what I mean?" Practice visualization and then teach your child visualization so they may see what you see—themselves untroubled, happy, and relaxed.

Turn on the Music

Literally, turn on your music. If you play an instrument, pick it up and play it. It is a known fact that music taps sensation in the human brain. This international language has the power to create a shift in mood. Lift yourself up with music. Play your favorite cheerful and pleasant music in your home.

"Music, Kitchen, Dance!"

"Still to this day I can hear the music when I walk through the side door of my home. Life seemed brighter when the music blared through that kitchen window. Mom smiled more than normal, dad danced more often and the rest of us loved life just that much more. When the music was turned up, the air smelled better, the colors in the room were brighter . . . it changed the entire aura of that house, indeed for the better. Not only did the music change the aura of

our home, it changed the rhythm of our souls. That mu-sic-filled kitchen became a happy place, a place to dance and a place to feel united as a family who shared a home and a tune. The music allowed for us to dance our butts off, to jump up and down hand in hand reminding us that we had commonality. It taught us how to love each other, how to laugh at each other again, the music brought it all back to how our family was created to be. So, turn up the music and get your groove on!"

– Written by an Adult Child Who
Still Hears the Music

Unconditional Love

Commit to unconditionally love your child (even when it's diffi-cult). Unconditional love is a choice to model a consistent love without judgment, even at times when you are disappointed with behavior or choices. Unconditional love sometimes requires tough love, but never prideful love, nor love given in return for actions of approval.

"Mom, what I really want is to know that at the end of the day I can come to you with anything and you will still love me."

– From a Teenager to Her Mom

Forgive and Learn

This does not suggest you forget and, by no means, should you bury your head and pretend something did not happen. Address with your child what happened, and if you're uncomfortable alone, you and your child can meet with a neutral third party. A good therapist is recommended.

We think it is critical to forgive. You will make mistakes. Forgive yourself. Do not hold yourself captive to self-ridicule, resentment, and/or grudges. Your child will make mistakes. Forgive them. Shaming your child is destructive. They already are feeling ashamed of themselves. Together, forgive and learn from the experience. Drop your guard, relinquish your pride, and calmly discuss the mistakes. Then, be proactive by applying the knowledge learned in the mistakes to change future happenings.

Open Eyes That Could Not See

"I did everything right. EVERYTHING. I read all the books, heard all the speakers, served on all the boards, chaired all the fundraisers. My central mission was to educate the world on addiction and disordered eating. Okay, maybe not the world but definitely my community. I have been a member of a Twelve Step recovery group since 2002. So how did I miss the fact that my beautiful teenager was suffering from binge eating disorder? She always seemed happy. She excelled in school. She was outgoing and involved. She was active and appeared healthy.

It took a separate family crisis to allow me to see the real pain our beautiful daughter was experiencing. I learned that shame has no place in recovery. I had to forgive myself for missing early signs of her disorder. There is hope all around us but you may miss it if you are burdened with guilt.

Our daughter began seeing a therapist. She would

Skype when she couldn't make appointments. She met with other young adults who had been down similar paths. To-day she openly shares her story of hope and self-love. I am in awe of her strength and courage."

— A Mom and Activist

Journal

Perhaps you will never share the written words of a journal with anyone, or perhaps you will share those recorded feelings with a therapist, a loved one, or a stranger. At the very least, the written word clears the mind, gives you a place to express your thoughts and feelings. Throughout your journey you can always go back and reference past events, milestones you experienced, and lessons learned. We found getting feelings and frustrations out on to the pages very therapeutic.

Seek a Mentor for your Child

When seeking out a mentor for your child, you may have a particular individual in mind, and/or you might want to ask your child whom they want as a mentor. If your child is in therapy, ask the therapist's advice.

Consider a family member (outside of the ones living in your home), a friend, a teacher, a coach, and/or a member of your village to mentor your child. Explain your intention to the potential mentor and be honest. Tell them why you feel your child needs a mentor and that you hope your child and the mentor will cultivate an additional adult relationship outside of you and/or your spouse. It is crucial that the mentor relationship is positive, confidential, safe, and loving. Be wise with who you ask to mentor your child. For the relationship to be successful, it is important for you to allow that relationship to grow between them without you constantly being involved. The mentor should know the child well enough to have an idea of what is supportive not destructive. For example, the mentor(s) can ask the child to join them for coffee or hot chocolate, a fun activity, a cultural event, a movie, a meal, a walk, etc., and you do not go with them. A shopping date is not recommended!

Confidentiality between the mentor and child is important. The mentorship is not to be seen as a place to gather information for the mom, unless of course, the information deals with consequential harm or the potential death of your child.

My Yoga Teacher

"I came to her a broken and entangled mess of a human. My soul was waging war against itself, riddled with anxiety and self-loathing. My perception of myself was drenched in hatred, disrespect, and frustration. I wanted to be different. I craved alteration and bathed in the concept that I would never be enough. I was sixteen.

I left her a new creation. I was strong. Clothed in worthiness and seeping with gratitude, I loved myself. I loved my body. My capabilities were now known to me, just as the body knows to breathe. They were obvious to me. The intricacy of my soul fascinated me, and I had so much more room in my head to practice compassion for others. I stopped apologizing for being magnificent.

What happened in between the time that we met and the time I left is beyond linguistic explanation. It was a *yoga practice I grew to love through the acceptance I felt on my mat. It was the way she taught me to give myself the praise I was looking to gain from others. It was how she had an uncanny ability to ooze wisdom and perspective into every conversation. It was the space she so gently held for me to unapologetically feel whatever was buried in that broken heart of mine. It was the belief she taught me to instill within myself. It was the way yoga infiltrated and applied to every aspect of life. It was the strength I found within my own body and the appreciation of ability discovered through movement. It was growth in the purest and most loving form. It was nourishment. It was healing.*

So when people ask me how I recovered from all of that wicked pain that used to lay dormant in my soul, I say my yoga teacher. I say yoga."

– A Mentee Who is Grateful For Her Mentor

Break and Re-Set

Give yourself permission to not be okay. Allow yourself to cry, to break emotionally, and to process your frustrations. Therapy is a safe and private place for that. A trustworthy friend who just allows you to emote and experience the emotions with no judgment and no intention of "fixing you" is always helpful. We, as parents, tend to believe that we must always be strong. It is not weak to cry; it is healthy as it releases the disappointment, anger, and/or resentment you potentially harbor when dealing with this merciless disease. And then, re-set!

It is also fair to discuss your frustrations with your child, but not in a cruel or mean-spirited manner. You are the adult and need to put restrictions around how you present your feelings and what you tell your child. Love prevails. Love is why we get so frustrated.

Make your House a "Home"

You have the ability to create an inviting space. We are not kidding about turning on your music! Help create the ambience you want to feel upon entering the home, whatever your space may be. Your children will notice! Create smells, sounds, and sights that are welcoming, warm, and feel safe. This is an opportunity to lighten up the mood a bit. There is a difference between a house and a "home."

Sleep

Literally. Sleep. Be wary of exhausting yourself and becoming fatigued. You will need your sleep to help you think straight and maintain control over your emotions whether at home, at work, or socially. Whenever, however you can prioritize sleep, please do.

Sense of Joy, Sense of Humor

As a mom, you do have the choice of how you will react to your child and all loved ones living in your home. Gretchen Rubin wrote a book called, *The Happiness Project*, as an approach to changing your life. "Your Project would look different from mine," she writes, "but it's a rare occasion a person can't benefit from a happiness project." What makes you happy? What makes you laugh? What brings joy to your life? Do you deliver the joy to others? No doubt, caretaking a child battling an eating disorder is extremely difficult, thus all the more reason you will benefit from rediscovering your joys and your sense of humor. You will rub off on those around you!

"Laughter makes the heart beat stronger. It gives your day purpose and your rest reason. Laugher gets your body moving, vibrating, sending out sensations that bring the light into the world. To laugh every day is to live every day. It's to heal, and to cope . . . it's how we made it through. In our family, we tried to remember the good, the blessings and the joy. Our laughter gave us presence, a hope to exist in a world that felt so sad at times. My grandmother once told me, "Never let your head hit the pillow without having laughed so hard your tummy hurts." Finding that joy again became the anthem of our story."
            – An Adult Child Who Loves to Laugh

Work, Play, and Passion

Work because you love it and/or work if you have to pay the bills and provide for your loved ones. Play because you love it; play to find joy in this life. Open your heart to passion, both physical and emotional. Be passionate because you love it. Be passionate to find the capacity of your heart. We must learn to allow ourselves to have the experiences that would make us passionate, and then, embrace them. Is your passion art, gardening, worship, music, writing, sharing time with friends, being outdoors, time with family, mission or humanitarian aid, volunteer work? Find and/or continue your passions. Do you need to create? Are you relational? Do you love to cook? Do you need to lie quietly under a tree? Enthusiasm, purpose, and positive energy does trickle down to your child. Please find your passions. Please live out your passions. You will be a better mother/caretaker when you do.

"So how does a person acquire passion? Well, honestly, I have come to find that a person cannot just buy it off a shelf, or get it from someone else. Passion comes from within oneself, but it can be found in all things. Hidden in places no one would dare to look, passion is found in simplicity but at the same time in intensity. See, passion is all in one's perspective. To be passionate about something does not mean that one has to do it all of the time or become their obsession. Actually it can be in something as simplistic as the sound of ballet shoes on the dance floor, seeing God's presence in someone else, the colors of the sunset, or simply just the sound of a familiar voice that makes one smile. It is not only influenced by extremes, passion is ambiguous."

— A Fifteen-year-old Girl

Get Out of the Eating Disorder "Obsession"

You, your child, and your family are more than this disease. Believe that you are stronger, wiser, and considerably more significant than an eating disorder. Obsessing over your child's issue is normal. The saying "Mama is only as happy as her most unhappy child" rings true for most of us. Yet, you do have the ability to discuss other topics of interest. Go do something together other than therapy, push yourself to find areas of commonality outside of constant eating-disorder conversation, and recognize there is more to life than constantly obsessing over the eating disorder. Obsessing gives the illness power!

> *"I would like to find another word in our vocabulary to replace 'eating disorder!' At times it feels so defeating and negative. Yes, it is excruciatingly painful at times, but my child is NOT an 'eating disorder.' She is more, I am more, and we are more."*
>
> — A Mom in the Trenches

Volunteer

The old saying goes, "You will receive more than you give." It is true. And, your child will witness your efforts and be affected by your choice of action. We suggest you volunteer outside of the eating-disorder world. (Please refer to chapter 14, "Service to Others.")

Become a Kinder Human Being. Teach Your Child to Become a Kinder Human Being

So, how does one become a kinder human being? Practice kindness, and the action of kindness becomes habitual! You first have to take care of yourself. Be kind to yourself. This is not being selfish; it is a necessity and may even be self-preservation. When you are depleted it is far easier to be angry, resentful, impatient, short-tempered, and frustrated, and then it is almost impossible to be kind to others. Treat yourself with the same tenderness you would show another; be gentle with yourself during this time.

Teach your child kindness by example. At first it takes intention, a conscious mind to remember to be kind. But in time it becomes a natural habit.

Communicate Honestly and Openly with Your Spouse/Partner/Significant Other

Lastly, but maybe most importantly, if you are married or in a committed relationship, getting on the same page with your spouse from the beginning will help you both stay grounded. We have witnessed marriages/partnerships where spouses support one another and thus stand stronger together. They help balance one another by fairly discussing issues surrounding the eating disorder, compromising, asking for help, offering help, and covering each other's responsibilities, especially when they have more than one child. This is preferable, helpful to your child's recovery, and a good example for the whole family. If you are in sync with your partner, that is fortunate.

We understand that life is not always smooth. Please know you are not abnormal if you and your spouse/partner feel a sense of discord. Of course, all adult relationships are unique, and no matter the status of your relationship, even a healthy relationship can deteriorate under this kind of stress. Often the pain of the situation will uncover issues in your marriage/relationship that need to be dealt with. When you are able, deal with the discrepancies. By nature, we are all created differently, thus our opinions come from our personal point of reference and life experience. This does not make you right or wrong, and it does not make your mate right or wrong. It confirms that your individual thought processes are different. Agreeing on best-case scenarios for your child is complex. Congruency takes patience, time, effort, and an open mind. Ask for help, tenderness, and love from your spouse, and in return, try offering it. Do not hesitate to get involved in marital counseling or parent support groups or to meet with and learn from other couples who have experience with the death grip of an eating disorder.

To the best of your ability, work diplomatically with your spouse/partner. Blaming one another for your child's issues is common, but don't be fooled—it is destructive and can lead to resentment. We know this from experience!

If your spouse/partner is not interested, overwhelmed, or simply cannot grasp the effects of the disease, do not freeze. We suggest you actively move forward and be intentional in informing them of the course of action you have chosen. Communicate honestly and remember that being kind and boldly honest with your spouse/partner will be much more effective than being hateful.

Realistically, being in union with your partner is beneficial but sometimes does not seem possible. You know your partner best and ultimately it is you, and often only you, who will know what steps to take to help yourself and positively aid in your child's healing.

We were not given instructions on how to parent. In some cases, we did not choose the issues at hand nor the timing. We may not have the opportunity to construct the picture-perfect life, but we do have the choice of how we will react to everything that crosses our life's path. Take time to help yourself, build your knowledge base, take care of your needs, and be kind to yourself in the process. By preparing your mind before the storm hits, maybe, just maybe, you will fair the choppy, unpredictable patterns with more grace and ease. Where can you start the process of preparing your mind? What do you yearn for? What makes you confident? What gives you peace? Please begin by making the time and space to be intentional with your mental preparation. The suggestions above are a good place to start. Then, add on specific ones to your lifestyle and individual needs.

Does This Feel Familiar?

A Father's Perspective

"It is with great humility that I attempt to explain a father's perspective of caring for and helping to raise a child with an eating disorder.

In the summer of 2005, my perspective of our family would have read like a storybook. Family of five, living in an upper-class neighborhood, good schools, lots of friends, well adjusted children and what I perceived to be a better than average marriage. I was thinking we were truly blessed and other than the normal trials and tribulations involved in raising young children, we were the luckiest people on planet earth.

In September of that year, our daughter was diagnosed with anorexia. Scared and uninformed, Mom and Dad sprung into action, however in very different directions. Mom with her emotional, nurturing, kind way and Dad convinced that it was only a matter of time until he found the solution to the problem. Initially, I discounted by wife's concerns as I was convinced that the entire situation was being blown way out of proportion. However, one month later, our daughter was hospitalized. It was then that we began to organize a well-educated and informed team of medical eating disorder professionals to assist and educate us with regard to this traumatic problem. As we listened and learned, we both began to formulate our own ideas and opinions which created a growing divide between the two of us. This divide and lack of communication developed into a change in what we had grown to know as normalcy in our family order and in our marriage. Eventually, as things worsened, all fingers were pointed at me and I became the cause of the problem and the underlying cause of the eating disorder. The divide grew wider!

Through numerous hours of individual and family therapy, I began to realize I could not change the past, I needed to let go of hurt feelings and join hands with my family, be an unselfish part of the solution. Throughout the therapy I began to understand that some of my parenting behavior was surfacing as an important factor in our daughter's insecurities. It took me awhile not to take these realizations as personal attacks because I knew that I would never hurt what I loved the most on this earth, my family. Though I know I did not cause an eating disorder, with the help of my wife, I did apologize and ask our sick child for forgiveness. We, our entire family, all asked forgiveness from each other and learned the importance of that. I now think the willingness to be vulnerable and asking for forgiveness provided us the ability to move forward.

A turning point for me was finally being convinced that an eating disorder is a mental illness and that every case is unique and different. We continued to push forward, with unrelenting devotion to our daughter and her brother and sister. Finally, with the understanding that I could not solve the problem, I began to soften and let go of the resentment I had formulated toward my wife. In hindsight, it was her intuition and incredible drive that had identified the issue and she had gotten us the help that we were all in need of. She dealt with and observed this problem all day, every day for weeks on end, for months, for years. During those early years, I would come home at night and profess to have a better idea or a different approach.

To fathers out there struggling, confused and or angry; listen to your wife, when you question the intuition of a mother do it gently and be as supportive and as non-combative as possible in times of crisis. Participate in therapy, listen and open your mind to a new world that you cannot initially understand!

Be fully engaged and supportive of your spouse, your sick child and your entire family, to the best of your ability. Over communicate with your children such that they can begin to understand the shift in parental attention and time. Most importantly, set your ego aside, recognize your limitations and tell your wife how much you love her each and every day, you have to be a team! Dads tend to get caught up in their jobs and outside responsibilities and we lose sight of how important it is for our children to feel the security and safety of a father's unconditional love.

Dads are trained to lead and to channel our energy to be logical thinkers and problem solvers. Unfortunately, this disease does not fit that strategy. I encourage each of you to recognize this fact early on and join hands with your spouse to learn how, together, you can best cope with the situation. Additionally, it will take the combined effort of you both to maintain some sort of normalcy in your family life at home, which by the way, is just as important as the resolution of the medical problem.

To the mothers and wives in the daily grind, connect with your spouse and recognize that fathers don't always have the innate intuition or understanding that mothers do. Over communicate with our spouse and attempt to unite in every aspect fighting this disease. Thinking your spouse does not understand or isn't emotionally capable of dealing causes resentment and has negative effects on the marriage and the children. I beg of you to work together, allow one another to voice their opinions, concerns, thoughts and focus on listening such that the best of mom and the best of dad will be exposed. Given the differences in the male and female psyche, this is easy to say and extremely difficult to put into action. If there is ever a time to put egos aside, now is the time. Move forward as a united team. This will provide the best support for your sick child and will provide the family environment your other children so desperately need. Not to mention, this unity will provide the foundation that your marriage needs to fight off the attack.

Following a tormenting ten-year journey with a daughter victim to an eating disorder, I can successfully report with great humility, that you can and will learn to cope with and control this horrible disease. Our daughter graduated from an Arts Magnate High School, moved completely across the United States, graduated from college in four years with honors and is now working and supporting herself. My sincere advice is to understand at the onset, there often is not a logical approach or definitive answer to dealing and coping with this mental disorder. It is often that we learn; what not to do.

I wish I knew in 2005, what I know now, but I encourage every dad who finds himself in this predicament to stay in the fight, stay involved, get educated on the disease and most importantly support your wife and her motherly intuitions. Your relationship with your wife, your sick child and your entire family will be better for it, as humility and support breed respect!"

– A Dad

5 STREAMLINE YOUR LIFE

[Streamlining your family priorities and work-related
responsibilities will help reduce the turbulence!]

Streamlining your family and your work will hopefully help increase the ease of healing more quickly and efficiently. Bluntly put, find an effective way to organize and prioritize the things that are vitally important in your life and your family's life. By family, we mean the immediate family that lives with you and/or adult children you see daily and those who have close contact with the person who has the eating disorder. Some family is chosen and not biologically related. Please see the suggestions below.

What Could a Mom Do Now?

Find the time to review your priorities. Write them down if need be and begin a sequential list from critical to less important. Balancing both your priorities and your family's priorities takes time and cannot be done overnight. Be patient with yourself but try to calculate your decisions. Take a look at your family and ask your-self, *What makes our house feel like a home? What comforts the family and makes them want to spend time at home? What can we let go of and/or change to function more smoothly during this difficult time?*

We have chosen two areas that are important and impactful to well-being: family and work.

Family

Families come in all different dimensions with varied band-width and experiences, never looking identical to another. What works for one may not work for another. However, when raising a child with an eating disorder there are some common family dynamics that seem to cross over most boundaries. If you are the parent to more than one child, have no doubt the family is in for a challenging ride. Committing to being honest up front with your spouse, partner, children, and loved ones will help you stabilize your mental faculties, reasoning, reac-tions, and judgment.

We also believe respect is a vital part to parenting. Gain your child's respect, and they will learn to respect you.

"The parent-child bond is the foundation on which all relationships are built. Especially, in and through the se-cured parent connection where a child learns how to love themselves and internalizes how they deserve to be treated by others. Treasure and nurture this bond like no other. Let your children know that you can make room for imperfec-tion, yours, and theirs, and that the very thing that makes them beautiful are their flaws and the unique essence that is they. Measure your love not in numbers but by their

character and intrinsic value. Be a reflection that they can be proud of when they look at themselves in the mirror and see what you have helped to create."
— A Mother, Wife, Daughter, and Therapist
Miki Johnston, MSW, LCSW

Below we have listed suggestions on how to help streamline the home and family.

- *Quality Time vs. Quantity Time.* The reality is that with a sick child, there is no equality of time. The sick child needs more. Do your best to focus on quality of time with your other children/family members. One example is, try to attend the other children's important events such as sports, school, arts, life celebrations, and occasions outside of the eating-disorder world that are seemingly important to them. When you let them down by not being present, help them understand the current situation by communicating lovingly and including them when appropriate. It is common for siblings and other family members to initially resent what the illness does to the family. Time and open loving communication with your children and family does help with sensitivity. Remind them to fight the disease, not their sibling.

- *Communicate.* Set aside time to talk as a family and address what's going on with each member. Be honest, be appropriately open, and be the adult in the conversation! Straight-forward talk with appropriate boundries can relieve tension and fear.

- *Share responsibilities with your spouse/partner.* Take turns tending to children's needs and household tasks, especially when your children are young. We have been most successful when we take the time to discuss these responsibilities considering whose personality is best at what: financial tasks, cooking, emotional nurturing, morning routine, late-night routines, or spontaneous decision-making. Prepare yourself to know you will have to care take in areas you feel inadequate in order to cover for your spouse. Serious lessons in give-and-take are easiest when communicating is respectful.

- *Engage your children and teach them to fend for themselves.* For example, set up chores, have children clean their rooms, make school lunches, help with errands, drive younger kids to events, help cook meals, etc. If you have preteens and/or teenagers, it is so important to give them responsibilities to help in the home. This makes them feel purposeful, and ultimately these responsibilities help them become independent and capable. Once they get used to the responsibilities they will actually like the independence. Hopefully, they will feel a sense of purpose and enjoy helping relieve you of the constant family duties. If not, they should still be required to help!

- *Keep a family calendar for everyone to see daily schedules.* Do you work better with a schedule? If so, keep a family list of "to dos" and post it where all can see and respond to. Have your children keep and make lists of what they are responsible for and need to accomplish during days of the week. Organize to the best of your ability a structured routine that feels steady and prudent when it comes to responsibilities in the home.

- *Keep a conscious mind with what chores are actually important!* For example, if a bed does not get made in the morning, decide if that is worth an exchange of harsh words. Could it be made in the afternoon?

- *Say no when possible to alleviate added pressure of a burdensome schedule.* Streamline by letting go of frivolous activities; it is okay to rein in the social calendar. When saying no to a child, remember that the delivery of the message substantially effects the reaction! A loving no with a fair explanation (even if it is short and to the point) is far more well-received creating mutual respect.

- *Say yes when possible to add some lighthearted fun to your lives.*

- *Ask for help from loved ones outside of the family.* These are family and friends you trust immensely.

- *Accept help from friends, extended family, and/or neighbors.* You cannot do it all, so if someone offers to lend a helping hand, consider saying, "Yes and thank you!" We have seen so many family members and friends who feel helpless. Allowing loved ones to help gives them the gift of helping, and that feels purposeful. Everyone wants to feel purposeful.

- *Listen.* What are the needs and wants of the family members? One of them just might have a wonderful idea or solution to an issue.

- *Family meetings.* Several of us moms have discussed the successes (and frustrations) of an arranged family meeting. Choose a day and time that is most suitable for everyone. Sit down in a comfortable place and discuss upcoming plans. This is a good time to set up a family calendar, listen, respond to your family's concerns, and share your thoughts. Keep the peace and remember that your disposition will help to set the mood of the family meeting. Do your best to be even-tempered.

"In retrospect, the experience did provide a huge knowledge of sensitivity in my other children, but not always at the time. Their frustrations and resentment then were valid."
— Mom of Five, One of Whom Suffered From an Eating Disorder

- *Acquire educational assistance if you are financially able.* Do not hesitate to get school tutors to help with homework and projects, most especially if you have children in high school. We believe this is an important suggestion as we are moms, not our children's high school and/or college professors. Ask for help from counselors, teachers, coaches, and, if necessary, the administration. You want your children to feel supported in their studies but honestly, education is a demanding area that requires a lot of parents' time. We suggest, if possible, get outside help.
- *Organize your family's daily routines to the best of your ability.* Ask the family to help.

"My family has a shoe drawer in our kitchen full of shoes. These are the shoes dropped on the floor after school or left under the homework table, in the yard, or on the floor the night before. That may seem silly but in the rush of the morning, our kids always get out of the door on time and with a pair of shoes on! We also have a toothbrush drawer downstairs in the kitchen. And, lockers by the back door for backpacks and a coat rack. A smooth morning looks something like this: Eat breakfast, brush your teeth at the

> *kitchen sink, get your shoes from the shoe drawer, grab the backpack that was packed the night before, get a coat, and the kids are off for school! The point being, we have had to create staging areas that may not seem typical but they work great for our family. And by the way, I too had to learn how to be more structured and organized!"*
> — A Mom Who is Not Typically Organized

- *Schedule family therapy.* Does it fit in your schedule? Probably not, but we highly recommend family therapy. Schedule family therapy for you and your family knowing it may take several weekly visits to the family therapist for an extended period of time, perhaps even three to twelve months. (Please refer to the "Getting Professional Help, Now" chapter of this book.)

- *Help yourself too.* Make an agreement with yourself to take care of yourself. Mentally and emotionally settle into the journey. Evaluate your priorities and be willing to shift if and when necessary. Sometimes when these shifts occur, you just might find peace in releasing what was once deemed so important and realizing that life's design feels more rewarding and meaningful when focusing on the consequential.

Work

Work is your job, and it's important for the well-being of your family and you. Potentially, your income is what supports the treatment for your loved one. Maintaining the balance between work and life can be very challenging, and it's a delicate balance—in particular, fulfilling the needs of the individual who's suffering from the eating disorder. If you conclude up front that the balance is going to be challenging, with conscious intention set up safety nets for success.

Below are fifteen suggestions to help you streamline your work:

- *Leave your work at the office so that when you are at home, you can focus on your relationships with those you love.* This is much easier said than done, especially if you are a creative type, the sole breadwinner, and/or you work from home. But willfully and with purpose, do your best to give full attention to your family when you are home.

- *If you're the creative type, include your family in your work when possible and ask their opinions*—like, for example, advice on the title of the book you're writing and/or helping with art projects.

- *Leave for work stress-free.* Do your best to set the atmosphere of the morning rush as peaceful and organized as possible. Try playing relaxing music and not the news. Consider preparing the night before, especially if you have young children, in order to start the workday more relaxed.

- *Use your time efficiently.*

- *Understand the company's policy regarding medical leave, time off, and flex-time.* Talk with the HR manager and review company policies.

- *Communicate.* Consider talking to your boss/partners/ colleagues up front and explain what the situation is with your child's eating disorder. Be honest, but don't be over-reactive and/or catastrophic in your explanation. We hope you will receive moral and emotional support.

- *Review the office insurance plan.* If you are covered by insurance at work, set up a meeting with the person(s) in charge of the plan. Educate yourself on your insurance coverage and how best to approach filing claims. (Please refer to the "Insurance" section of this book in regards to insurance benefits offered/carried by your employer.)

- *If you are the boss, with integrity, let your assistants know that more will be required of them during this time.* Ask colleagues who you trust to fill in when absent.

- *Confirm times away from your job for therapy.* In other words, if you need to take three to four hours off once or twice a week, set it up to the best of your ability from the beginning. Get it on your schedule!

- *If your work is portable, take it with you.* You will have downtime waiting on your child—for example, waiting to pick them up as they finish a therapy session, during travel if you have to go elsewhere for help, or sitting in the waiting rooms of therapists, doctors, and/or nutritionists.

- *Say no.* Respectfully, decline extracurricular work-related events/activities. Spend time at home instead or spend some time alone to rejuvenate, however that works best for you.

- *Be prepared for emergencies.* When dealing with eating disorders and mental health, there will potentially be emergencies that pull you out of work. Have a Plan B/backup plan in place should you have to suddenly leave.

- *Connect with your family during downtime at work.* If possible, check in with your children and loved ones during lunch, coffee breaks, travel, etc. A simple but thoughtful and/or encouraging text feels good to receive.

- *Use technology to benefit your needs.* For example, Skype, video conference, FaceTime etc. with therapists and doctors when necessary. And, use telecommunication when possible to perform the same work skills at home with the equal performance. Consider less office time and more home time.

- *Encourage your child to work!* In few cases, a child can work for and/or with a parent/caregiver/mentor. This is a personal choice for you. Sometimes getting a paid job outside of the home or family—of course this is age-dependent—can bring about a sense of purpose and responsibility. It can also help the individual abstain from obsessing. Be wise in helping your child choose a job or volunteer work.

> *"Therapy is a lifesaver for so many millions of human beings that I would never discount its purpose in this world. But, sometimes, I believe therapy, especially talk therapy, can become part of the problem. The constant discussions about "me" has to make a child continually think about "me!" So, why not come up with solutions for "me" that aren't necessarily about "me?" This is why I wonder if work is one positive solution. Often I say to my kids, "go volunteer" but often that is self-gratifying and becomes a "me" subject again. But work, that is a place where you have responsibilities and people depend on you to do your part. In a sense, it's required of you."*
>
> – A Mom

Work may be using your acquired skills, a creative outlet for your mind, a purposeful benefit for our world, or perhaps just a job that pays the bills. But, not everything should be measured in economic value. For many, success is measured by the amount of money one makes, but true bona fide success is measured in relational meaning, relationships. Reviewing this ideology heeds the notion of balance between life and work related to our personal journeys. It's important to take a step back and reevaluate our relationship with work and the relationships in our families. Fulfilling our responsibilities to our family is necessary, and that means both financially and emotionally.

> *"One of the things I found interesting is that my sister received disability for her anorexia. Because of this she did not work. That was a curse! If she had worked she would have been forced to get out into the world and would not have been so isolated. Would have helped her feel a sense of purpose!"*
>
> – An Adult Sister

It's an intricate balance. The stability of work helps sustain the equilibrium of the family structure, and yet, it cannot buy love. Love is free to give. Love is free to receive. Love outweighs any paycheck, and the return is invaluable. Parenting a child with loving deliberateness will potentially be your most important life's work. The effects play out for generations to come!

Does This Feel Familiar?

A Grandmother Looks Back

"The first time my daughter called me to come see if I saw something 'wrong'

with her daughter, I was not upset as my granddaughter seemed the same as always, very animated, peppy and smiling. Then, I witnessed a major breakdown of not just tears but unreasonable distress over what seemed to be a very minor episode. It had to do with a text or a call from a friend and my granddaughter's skewed perception of what another person thought of her. I tried to put it off as pre-menstrual or teenage drama. However, as time went on I realized these out of control emotional breakdowns were not going away. From the outside (and I was kept on the outside for some time) it looked like something my granddaughter needed to get a grip on and just get over. As I watched my own daughter completely change, going from open to secretive, I realized the problem was both overwhelming and consuming to her. She watched helplessly as her daughter's condition deteriorated. Not that she was not trying. She educated herself and got professional help, but it was that the professional help did not seem satisfactory. Finally, I was brought into the problem of my granddaughter's eating disorder. I asked to go to the psychiatrist where my granddaughter was being treated so I could better understand my role to help my daughter and my granddaughter.

My husband and I met with my granddaughter's doctor, and I must say it was not very helpful. I was told to never discuss food or what she ate or the way she was handling her food by waddling it up, very peculiar to see and ignore. I tried to be in her life when possible. I was helping to pick her up from school and occasionally take her for treatment, anything to relieve my daughter when viable, as there are other children in the family. I think back on this and can say, I felt completely helpless as a contributor to the health of my granddaughter.

We have a large family and often have gatherings around a meal for birthdays, etc. at our home. This meant many cousins, aunts, uncles and friends all gathered around the table. I asked my daughter what foods to have in the house that my granddaughter might eat. I tried to have the few things I know she might eat in the refrigerator. She would always say she had eaten at home but after looking in the fridge would ask if she could have the apple, yogurt or some of the things she would touch.

My reaction, because of what I was told NOT to do, was almost ignoring that anything was going on. This was not easy and caused me to feel very estranged from my granddaughter and my own daughter. As my daughter worked very hard reading and talking to professionals she was able to express what was happening and help me understand this is like an addiction and must be worked out very carefully and there is NO QUICK FIX. The concern of this large family was great as the rest of the family felt the child took all of the attention to the detriment of her younger siblings. They were often home alone while Mother, Dad and their sister were at the doctors, psychiatrist or therapists. This caused much consternation of my other children and my husband.

If I could change anything about my role it would have been to press my daughter as to what I could do to relieve her with her chores and ask to help more with the other children. Looking back, I think she was slow to ask me too often to help her. I think she was trying to protect me by leaving me alone and not asking too many "favors." She was trying to handle it all quietly to protect her child and not have the stigma of Anorexia labeled on her child. The "Open Book" policy is the only way to go and yet I realize when it is your own child you do not want the rest of your friends and children of your friends to say she has an eating disorder, particularly with the name anorexia. Once my daughter was able to be open and honest with others, the clarity of how she handled the problem was wonderful because she no longer feared what others would say. She has gone on to be able to help many other mothers that call her as they go through this struggle with their children and benefitted them with what she has learned.

As a Grandma, one of the things I realize as a model for my own daughters and granddaughters is how we talk about our own image of ourselves. I have never been overweight but I do have a tummy and I have often fixated on how I look in clothes. This is our culture and how we perceive what is the way to "look." This is taken in from childhood and reinforced by ads in magazines and models or movies. I probably tried to control my own children from eating too many sweets. I wish I had just been more into cooking very healthy meals with no discussion about it and they would just learn to eat all things, in moderation.

I am watching this granddaughter who is now a young woman show her strength and I realize, she can and is handling her problem without constantly relying on her doctors and counselors. She has great faith and is very smart (this brightness and demanding of self often is part of the addictive personality). She has learned to accept herself and her self-image. This is beautiful to watch. Time and her strength are on her side. She is healthy and happy and now truly seems to know that she is capable of handling this illness."

– A Grandmother

6 SELF-REFLECTION

[Honest questions we must ask ourselves.]

As we have shared throughout this book, it is beneficial to seriously look at our own actions and motives. As we shared in the introduction: "Over the years and on several occasions, the women writing this book have all had to look into our own mirrors and, at times, make changes. We've had to seek personal help from therapists and counselors. Sometimes it was difficult to see fallibility, yet we are grateful and better for that work."

There are few things in life that are guaranteed, but two absolutes are: 1) No one is perfect, and 2) Everyone experiences pain. We make mistakes, fail, and disappoint ourselves and others. No matter what, this is the human condition. And though we are not perfect, we do have free will and the ability to make choices and respond to the pain of life. Holding on to a prideful ego refusing to learn from our own personal mistakes is debilitating. Maybe it is not ego, but fear!

> *"The pain, the fear, the sorrow, the loneliness, the helpless-ness, the self-doubt, the questioning, the hatred and the anger all exist on this lane I have and will continue to voyage across. But I also recognize that with all of the dark comes tremendous amounts of light. For I also feel joy, love, enthu-siasm, bliss, peace, contentment, gratitude, compassion, and empathy as well. The light fails to exist without the dark. So though this road is often viewed as scary, I see that it will be and always has been my greatest teacher."*
>
> – Diary of a Victim of Anorexia

If we look at self-reflection as learning more about who we are, doing it should help us decide the best ways to handle pain and disappointment. It will help fill in the blanks to the blindside of life we do not currently understand. Re-evaluating our own actions, motives, and personal characteristics will feel vulnerable, and yet these steps towards a happier life are freeing. We know— all of us have been there! We as the writers of this book are par-ents, aunts, uncles, children, sisters, brothers, and grandparents. We are you. So please, be honest with yourself, with your closest loved ones, and the professionals you work with in helping you help yourself, thus helping your child to help herself!

> *"I had never been to therapy, I had no friends nor family with an eating disorder. I was totally in the dark and ig-norant in this very unfamiliar world of anorexia. Within a few months it came to my attention that the way I spoke about my body, referenced my size, my looks and my eating*

habits were an unhealthy example for my child of twelve. Maybe unconscious, but comments said were with a bit of sarcasm. Sadly, she listened, she heard, she saw, and she reacted."

– A Mom Who Wishes She Could Do It Over

What Could a Mom Do Now?

Answer the self-addressing questions below. Some of the questions might feel invasive, complicated, and/or potentially difficult to answer. Self-reflection does not mean you are "doing it wrong," nor should you feel belittled by this request; it is a healthy process. If you have not dealt with mental/emotional disorders, learning how to respond, react, and get motivated in a positive manner will help minimize frustration and miscommunication.

We have answered some of these questions, but you know yourself best and must answer in good faith being accountable to your own self. Here are ten self-reflective questions and suggestions.

Do I Continue to Add to My Child's Eating Disorder?

You know from chapter 2 of this book, "What Causes an Eating Disorder?" that you did not "cause" your child's eating disorder. But, yes, we can amplify the issue. Most likely, your adding to your child's problems is not intentional. There is a blindside to all human beings, and that is why it is critical for parents to self-reflect and educate themselves. We all have actions within our parenting style that need attention, and it's well-advised to get the advice from a professional on how to more suitably deal with your child's emotional issues as well as your own. Be open to personal adjustments and the time necessary to evolve into the parent your child needs. Obtaining the parent-child relationship you desire takes work from both you and your child.

Be an advocate for your child as a role model, dependable adult, listener, and forever, yet boundary-conscious, parental caretaker. Be non-judgmental, non-biased, and an educated mother. Fight the disease, not the child.

Does My Spouse, Partner, and/or My Family Unit Add to the Eating Disorder?

Research suggests that our children are born with a pre-disposition, making them more susceptible to the illness. Many, many children around the world who are in dire circumstances do not develop eating disorders, and children from happy, healthy homes full of love and support do develop eating disorders. (If you feel it is necessary, please review chapter 3, "Genetics.") Yet family problems can contribute to a potential eating disorder. Look at the interaction within the family and the family's dynamics regarding behavior towards one another. There is absolutely no excuse for abuse, be it sexual, physical, or verbal. That is an absolute.

How do you speak to one another? Are you careful not to favor one child over another? Are you and your spouse/partner setting a caring/loving example? Do you respect each family member? Do you smile? Do you touch? Do you offer up kind words? Are you grounded in your decisions about self and family?

How do you deal with confrontation? Do you push back when you know the situation is wrong? Do you allow cruel behavior from yourself and/or others?

Hateful, demeaning, neglectful, hostile interaction is never useful.

How Can I Be a Benefit to My Child's Healing Rather Than a Hindrance?

Have patience! Listen and then stand firm in your compassion-ate parental discipline and boundaries. The family unit is always complex. Good parenting should be based in love, and with ex-perience, we do get better. Do not settle into believing your child will always have an eating disorder and/or that your family is unable to evolve into a more functional, loving unit. Everyone in the family has to do the work. The work begins with knowledge. The work should always be based in love, not in ego or control.

Try not to be defensive or resist new ideas. Relinquish the guilt and keep moving forward, understanding that it may be three steps forward and one step back, sometimes you level out, and sometimes you might even go backwards. Always keep your eyes locked on the bigger picture—a healing, well-adjusted, and healthy child. Set it in your mind's eye now that healing will hap-pen. Your perception of how you see yourself in the role as a parent will affect the way your child will respond to you.

- *Set boundaries intended to keep your child safe.* Positive bound-aries are not a parental "power-play," and we know the difference within our own selves. Safe, positive boundar-ies take more explanation and time. Your child eventually recognizes your intentions are on their behalf, and they do feel safe.
- *Speak with firm, but loving, words.* Mind your words in a ma-ture and reflective way. Your voice is powerful—both pos-itively and negatively.
- *Establish a relationship of respect.* Respect is a two-way street.
- *Listen without judgment.*
- *Be an example.* We hear this all the time, but how do we

really implement being an example? Body language is the first impression; a frown, unhappy expression, lack of touch, and crossed-arms says it all in a second. Being an example begins with how we manage our adult demeanor.

Do I Celebrate the B or Demand an A+?

It is critical that our children know perfection is unrealistic. We keep saying this because perfection is a driving force behind eating disorders. Therefore, it is important to be very aware of your expectations and standards set upon your loved ones. We must ask ourselves if it is our journey we are expecting our children to forge, or is it their own? If you are raising a millennial, you might already understand that almost all of them see the world differently than we do. They are the first global-citizen generation, and success is more about meaning than it is about money or stature. Do you agree, and/or do you see this in your own children? Are you meeting them where they are?

When your child comes home with a B, are you disappointed? And if so, why? Is average not good enough? Frustration is fair if your child is simply not trying, but inevitably, there is a reason for that. Is the bar set too high? No one sets the bar higher for themselves than individuals struggling with eating disorders (they're perfectionists). When you set the goals, are you telling them you believe in them, or are you setting up a mandate that is rigid and often unattainable? Discernment in accountability and ethical standards is different than adhering to our societies' competitive A+ standards. No one can be the "ideal child," be it what they look like, how awesome they appear on paper, and/or how they manage their emotions. Just like us, our children continue to learn, all the while preserving their place in the world and where they fit. By no means should we enable apathy, self-hatred, or harmful behavior, and there are times it is our responsibility to intervene. Helping them navigate their journey, both with failure and winning, includes loving them despite their human flaws.

Perhaps the most important question is, Does your child's performance somehow reflect upon you as a parent/person? If we are honest, the answer is "yes," and you are not alone. We have all felt this judgment, especially when it is our child with the mental disorder.

Sharing our hopes, prayers, dreams, and wishes with our children is wonderful, but don't we have to allow them to have their own? Work by their side to support them knowing sometimes you have to dig down deep to hold them up. Help children learn to help themselves. Let them find out who they really are and where they fit in this world. They may or may not be that A+ kid, but they are yours—uniquely created and placed in your care to teach, love, and support as they find their way.

Under Pressure

"I always knew it was my responsibility to look the part, to be the personification of my parents' hopes and dreams. The unnatural battle between being me and pleasing them, was not apparent to me until years after I left my eating disorder. I say left because for many years it was my trusted life preserver, keeping me afloat, while anchoring my emotional growth and self-knowledge. My relationship with food was dependable when nothing else was. I could control something, and the scales measured my success.

Women living without fear of judgment were a mystery to me. Realizing I could set my own goals, cultivated from personal instincts and desires, was the first step toward reclaiming my lost childhood. The greatest challenge was deprograming the alarm bells, reminding me to care how others viewed me, more than I did myself.

If you love someone struggling with anorexia, listen to them. Actively seek knowledge about who they are, and help them learn to dream their own dreams. Look into their eyes and smile — make sure they believe it is their perfectly unique self you love, not an image. Encourage and celebrate authenticity. Try not to offer unwanted advice. We are hyper-aware of our faults, fighting to trust our inner voice. You can hardly imagine the burden. Don't value thinness. We know when you are faking it, so truly take the time to examine your relationship with appearance. Appreciate the gift this person is in your life, and become their champion. Say you are sorry if you wish you had done things differently. Own your part, and help them know their mistakes are of the past, only useful as a launch pad on a journey toward new strength. Mend wounds with laughter, tears and forgiveness. Stumbling is natural. We are just humans, doing our best to be real."

— Now a Loving Mom of Teenage Boys

Am I Using My Child's Successes to Make Up for My Own Lack of Purpose?

A child does not want to be your trophy. Nor does a child need a parade for every "so-called" accomplishment. Average can actually be very good, even in this highly competitive world. Consider reframing your understanding of success both for your child and yourself. Many of us were taught the definition of success was based on how much money we made and stature within our society. As we stated above, our children's millennial generation wants meaning and purpose.

If you feel a lack of purpose or boredom with who you have become, again, you are not alone. Sometimes we lose our way and forget who that person was before the childrearing years. Yet, do not use your child's potential achievements to fulfill your lack thereof, be it sports, artistic talent, or academics. That kind of conveyance puts undue amounts of pressure on children. Instead, go recreate yourself and rediscover who you are and who you want to be.

> *"See my soul not just a body. I am a human 'being' not a human 'doing.' I need to know that there are no conditions required of me to be loved by you. I need that mom, I really do."*
>
> – From a Child Recovering From an
> Eating Disorder to Her Mom

Have I Asked for Support from My Family?

You will personally benefit from the support of a spouse, partner, and mentally healthy family members.

Loving Someone Right Where They Are

> *"I truly never saw my role in the healing of the eating*

disorder as anything other than being supportive and loving someone right where they are. I listened. I learned. And am still learning. I think I just wanted to be there. And sometimes that meant to sit in silence. Or to provide a few minutes of space and breath. A presence. I never felt I contributed much. But less, can be more. And silence can be golden. Knowing that another human is there, feeling your pain, loving you and your child unconditionally, non-judgmentally provides relief. However brief. Presence in the moment at times says much more than all the words one can string together.

There is a definite ebb and flow with this disease. A forward movement, then retreat, growth, then a complete standstill. No two people heal at the same pace or in exactly the same way, but they heal. Given the right tools, environment, support and time. Lots of time. Patience.

Being a wingman. That was my role in all of this. I was a small part of the support team. No one gets through this anorexic journey alone. We all have a part, a role to play. And all the roles are important.

What doesn't kill us makes us stronger and all of those surrounding us, stronger too! "

– An Aunt

If you have other children, they will be affected. For many of us, it is challenging (often taxing and unnatural) to ask for support. In loneliness, we stay stuck in feeling like we have failed. Truth is, being a mother does define us (perhaps not entirely but it does), and innately we are programmed to "fix" problems within our families and solve issues. So asking for help can feel negative. But once you say it out loud, the disease becomes real. You are freed. Try to embrace an eating disorder as a disease and not as parental failure. Honesty and family therapy is recommended.

Have I Built My Village of Support?

As with the instinct of an animal, we moms feel the urge to carry the burdens of our offspring upon our shoulders. The arduous weight often transfers into pain and fear. Yet, we do have a choice of how we perceive and react to our child's burdens. In chapter 6, "Preparing Your Mind," we suggest you build a village of support. No matter how strong you are, we as women are not created to live alone. Confide in others who love you, especially those who love without judgment. Find a place to release your frustrations as well as people to bounce ideas off of. Build your own village of support.

Can I Love Unconditionally?

We define unconditional love as the choice of modeling a consistent love without judgment. It sometimes requires tough love, but never prideful love, nor love given in return for actions of approval. Are you capable? Can you make a conscious decision (and commitment) to love your child no matter the circumstance, outcome, and/or conditions both good and bad? Can you love your own self unconditionally? If not, seek help in understanding what this means and how to bring unconditional love into play. It is a choice, a clear decision we make, when we commit to love unconditionally. It sounds romantic and easy, but in reality, unconditional love is a learned behavior, a patterned habit. Sometimes the most loving things you do for your child are not the easiest things.

I Need You No Matter What Today Feels Like

"Dear Mom,

First of all, let me start by saying I need help. I need you to be my advocate because I am currently incapable of being my own. I am scared and depressed. I am captive to my own mind, and am imprisoned by this disease. Here are a few things I want you to know . . .

Don't let anyone tell you that I will deal with this for the rest of my life.

Set my weight much higher than you think is necessary. Doctors give you the bare minimum weight and call it 'healthy.' However, metabolism, muscle, thyroid, hormones, medication etc. all influence weight and I will forever be a prisoner to the scale if you set my weight too low.

Don't let me count calories. This is adding fuel to the fire that is destroying me. If you want me to be happy and healthy, you will keep me from this addictive habit. If I start counting now, I will still be counting the calories in my wedding cake and feeling guilty versus focusing on the joyous celebration. That is hell, and I don't wanna ever be there. Protect me please.

Help me to accept my body. Whether I'm ten pounds heavier or lighter my body's shape is the same. The sooner I recognize that my body is the way it is will be one step closer to recovery and healing.

Do not let me replace obsession with food for obsession with exercise. This is simply another method of controlling my body and will simply replace an unhealthy obsession that already exists. Help me to find my worth in different places, and to have a healthy and balanced relationship with exercise.

I am not myself, so please don't take anything personally. This disease will change me into someone you don't know. Do not worry, this is temporary. Know that I love you.

Please don't let me stand in front of a mirror. It does nothing good.

Throw away the scales in the house.

Keep me accountable and set boundaries. I will be pissed at you initially, but I promise I will thank you later. This is actually how I am going to feel the most loved and valued by you. I need you to be firm and stand strong.

Set a healthy example. I watch everything you do. If you aren't loving your body, why would I love mine?

Help me to redefine "health." Health and strength come in every size. Help me to let go of Americanized ideals of what being "healthy" looks like and help me to learn that size is predetermined at birth apart from my physical health.

I need your tough love Mom. You are going to have to make some really difficult decisions regarding my health. FIGHT for me. Ultimately I want freedom, so do not give up on me. Please. I will give you hell as you try to help. Know that this is not me. It's the disease. I love you so much, please keep loving me . . . So please fight for my freedom . . . And ours."

— From a Teenager Who is Now
a Recovered, Healthy Woman

Do I Need to Engage in Therapy for Myself as a Mom?

Yes, we recommend it. We all have been to therapy. Be open-minded with the personal therapist you choose and in the therapeutic setting. There is blindness to all of us, and learning to see ourselves fully is rewarding. Your openness will allow for further knowledge, change, and new experiences. There may be behaviors that you can adjust. These adjustments will aid to your growth as a parent and also benefit your child. Find a therapist who agrees to have a relationship with your child's therapist. Be honest, be open, be unguarded, and above all, be genuine. This includes being vulnerable. (Please see chapter 8, "Getting Professional Help for Yourself, Now.")

A Mom's Body Image Issues Affected Her Daughter's

"A new client sits across from me. She's fourteen, blonde haired, blue eyed, a freshman cheerleader with a long history of gymnastics and dance. The mother made the appointment due to her teenager's "moodiness." (Doesn't that come with the teenager territory? I kid . . . sort of . . .) After a few minutes with the daughter, I learned of her rampant body image issues, her restrictive eating, her excessive exercise routine and her anxiety regarding the constant competition she felt pressured to keep up with. She was depressed and bordering on an eating disorder diagnosis. Mom minimized the symptoms, brushing these behaviors off as "normal teenage worries." One day when leaving my office, the daughter

asks, "Can we get a sandwich on the way home?" The mother softly responds, "Oh Honey, you know I'm not eating carbs right now. If you're so worried about your weight then maybe you should do the same," gently touches her daughter's arm and walks toward the elevator. In that moment, her daughter's expression, the seemingly innocent mother's matter of fact attitude towards the shaming statement she just projected onto her daughter, it became clear that the teenager didn't only feel pressure from her peers but from her parent as well. These seemingly subtle comments became more and more frequent in my presence. Mom minimized her daughter's symptoms because she too experienced them. Instead of empathizing with her child, she denied the severity of her child's feelings in an attempt to normalize her own. Mothers often forget that they can project their own body image issues onto their children. Parents, often unknowingly and unintentionally, create an environment where children learn to criticize, even hate, their own bodies. I no longer view body image as an individual issue. It's a systemic issue."

– Mary Grace Mewett, Licensed Professional
Counselor, MS, LPC, NCC

Am I Fighting This Battle Alone? And for What Am I Fighting?

You will find yourself fighting for your own sanity as well as your child's freedom from the terror of an eating disorder. Fight for health, and do not get lost in the battle of worrying what others think, saving face, or covering up something you feel portrays you as weak. It's not worth your energy. If you are fighting this battle alone, ask for help. Do you think you are a control freak? Someone who thinks they know all the answers? If so, you are not alone. It seems to be common amongst us moms. Consider surrendering to the importance of consulting a certified eating disorder specialist, and then implement their professional suggestions. The fight together is easier, more productive, and not as scary.

> *"When I'm asked what it was like, what did I do, what were the signs, I take a deep breath and try to convey that this is not your fault; you did not cause this. Your child is struggling, conflicted, confused, likely pissed off, and in their attempt to deal with these overwhelming emotions, they seek control. It becomes about helping them face what they are trying so desperately to conceal. They have the key they just don't know it's in their hand. Research, ask questions, seek professional help but above all reassure and remind them how fiercely they are loved."*
> – A Mom Who Knows Love is Victorious

Does it take a lifetime to fully know ourselves? With every turn of event and new challenge, will we always respond the same? Do we continue to evolve through our lives and if so, what does that feel like? The power of introspective work allows us the time to consciously increase our purpose and become the individual we aspire to be. Please take some prayerful/meditative time to think through this chapter and the questions in chapter 3. In the long run you will be glad you did.

Does This Feel Familiar?

I Was the Wingman

"A decade later, I am still here. Always will be. The precious child who once suffered from anorexia has grown into a beautiful and productive young woman. I understand her and she me . . . kindred spirits. Her mother has often laughed and said her daughter came out of the wrong uterus. But in reality, I think God knew best when he gave her the mother he did. Anorexia takes patience, perseverance, stamina, lots of courage and the ability to communicate your own needs, as well as the needs of your child. My sister-in-law is a master at "getting to the bottom line."

I love my sweet niece, scars and all. She certainly doesn't need or want constant contact . . . we tag up, touch base. She knows I would drop everything for her at a moment's notice. The beauty is a decade later she and her parents don't need a wingman anymore.

One learns an awful lot about people's character, integrity, when trudging through life. Do they give up, walk away or dig in deep? Educate themselves and those around them or bury their head in the sand.

Fathers play such an important role in the healing of the anorexic. No one is prepared for this role, least of all "the daddy." My brother dug deep. Deeper than he ever dreamed, I can assure you that. He was always there. Present, listening intently. Loving unconditionally. He now has a relationship with his daughter, wife and two younger children that he probably wouldn't have otherwise. Certainly, he would give it all up to erase the pain, the tears, the self-loathing. Did the entire family suffer at the hands of the anorexia? You bet. Big time. But it has made each one the person they are now. Compassionate, empathetic and understanding of others with a far deeper capacity for love than most of us can begin to comprehend. Watching someone you adore tormented by a disease you don't understand and can't repair changes your life perspective forever.

My brother and sister-in-law have been kind enough to share their precious children with me. Our families are extremely devoted, sharing in each other's pain and triumphs . . . wanting nothing more than to love and support each other, unconditionally. Knowing your family loves you completely and always has your back allows you the courage to stretch, to heal."

– An Aunt

NOTES

NOTES

NOTES

NOTES

WHAT DO I NEED TO DO?

"The cycle is self-obsession, for I think the world is looking at me, but I suppose this is simply how I interpret it to be. No matter hatred or narcissism, it is one and the same. Self-abuse, a form of self-obsession, is a trepidation-inducing game. Fear will keep you locked in the castle of your mind . . . waiting for a Prince Charming to tell you that you're worthy of his time. But this life is NOT ABOUT ME . . . no . . . so my proposition is as follows: Filling body, mind, and soul with self-hate leads to nothing but an existence that is hollow. But here is an idea, clothed in a new lens, dripping with truth."

– From the Diary of a Teen Battling Anorexia

7 FOR YOUR CHILD, NOW

[
It's not just about food. Recovery is about developing into the person you want to be. Worthy. Purposeful. Validated. Knowledgeable. Connected. Loved and Loving.
]

Getting professional advice for your child is potentially your most consequential responsibility as the parent. No matter the effort, positive intention, and unconditional love, you cannot fix your child's eating disorder alone. You, your child, and your family members need to learn the coping tools necessary to aid in your child's recovery as well as that of the family. We believe it is imperative that you and your family are involved in your child's therapy in a healthy, productive way. Healthy, productive ways may include individual therapy, therapy with the caregivers and the individual struggling, and/or family therapy. Educating yourself by reading this book is a great start.

If your child is over eighteen years old, and they are willing, we recommend they sign a waiver to allow interaction between you and their doctors and therapist. Adult children are just that: adults who need to be accountable for themselves, but if your adult child's life is in danger, you need to intervene. Most of us moms participating in this book understand that there are times our adult children are incapable of making logical decisions due to the grip of the disease.

So where do we began? If your child is old enough to understand, ask them what they need, how they feel about therapy, and open up a discussion on those possibilities. Your delivery, body language, and mood matters as you discuss the feasibility of introducing therapy into their life, your life, and that of the family. You can be inflexible in your decision and demand therapy, but walking them through the gate of understanding as to why you feel so strongly seems to be most effective approach.

What Could a Mom Do Now?

You probably know your child better than anyone. If you are concerned, do not procrastinate. There is every reason in the world why therapy does not fit into our busy scheduled lives, but find the time and space. It is worth the effort. If your child had a broken leg, would you hesitate to take them to a doctor? Mental health is as equally, if not more, important. It can be complicated, but this is your child's life we are talking about. Below are fourteen suggestions for being pro-active in securing professional help for your child.

Medical Emergency

If you believe your child is in medical danger, take them to the nearest emergency room immediately. The team of ER doctors will evaluate your child, and depending upon the severity of the condition, the doctors will admit your child into the hospital and/ or give you reasonable referrals. If they do not give you sound advice you are comfortable with, ask until you get the help you believe your child needs.

Early Intervention

If you recognize (or think you recognize) the signs of an eating disorder in your child, take it seriously from the beginning and move forward in an active, productive way. Statistics prove that the earlier the intervention, the higher potential for healing.

Understand the Types of Therapists and Eating Disorder Professionals Available

There are thousands of "therapists," and the task to hire one can be tiresome. Be relentless but speedy until you find the right fit. We recommend you stay within the eating-disorder community of health care providers in your area. Here are some categories we can recommend:

- *Eating-disorder psychiatrists:* Medical doctors (MDs) who are licensed to prescribe medications and manage drug therapy. Psychiatrists are trained extensively and knowledgeably in the unbelievable complexities of psychiatric drugs. Psychiatrists are able to treat co-existing disorders with medication, but to date, there is no medication that cures an eating disorder. Some psychiatrists also conduct regular therapy sessions.
- *Licensed therapists specializing in eating disorders:* Eating-disorder psychologists, PhD's, eating-disorder counselors, social workers, faith-based therapists, family therapists. We recommend you engage a "licensed professional." These therapists provide regular therapy sessions, group therapy, and family therapy and may also treat co-occurring disorders in their practice.

- *Physicians who specialize in treating eating disorders:* We recommend these MDs work in conjunction with your child and/or family therapist. They oversee medical complications that arise from eating disorders like heart problems, muscle atrophy, migraines, osteoporosis, etc.
- *Registered dieticians and nutritionists:* Please refer to chapter 9 for details outlining the role of dieticians and nutritionists.

We felt most successful when working with a "treatment team"—the psychiatrist, dietician, medical doctor, and therapist who collaborate on behalf of your child and family. The therapist, working with the person healing from an eating disorder, is usually the team leader/point person. The team varies depending on the type of treatment, severity of illness, your family structure, etc. Find what works best for your child and family.

Have a Professional Assess Your Child's Health

If you suspect or know that your child has an eating disorder, have your child assessed by a licensed eating disorder professional who can officially diagnose him or her. We recommend that you do not diagnose your child. Keep in mind, some pediatricians and/or primary care physicians are not well-versed in eating disorders, but they can give you a solid referral.

- Ask your child's pediatrician for a referral to a licensed professional who specializes in eating disorders.
- Ask any persons you know who are familiar with eating disorders and have experience and/or are currently dealing with the issue for a referral.
- Use your village of support and ask for help.

- Call the National Eating Disorders Association Helpline. (Please refer to the appendix in the back of this book for details.)
- For a free crisis counselor contact the National Eating Disorder Association. (Please refer to the appendix in the back of this book for details.)
- Contact the Crisis Text Line. (Please refer to the appendix in the back of this book for details.)
- Search for treatment in your area of the country at EDReferral.com. (Please refer to the appendix in the back of this book for details.)
- Visit the website of the National Association of Anorexia and Associated Disorders at www.anad.org.

*If all else fails, go to the nearest emergency room and ask for help.

Understand the Intentions of Therapy

It's a plus if you are well-versed in therapy. You are well on your way. If you are unfamiliar with therapy, we think it's important to try to educate yourself before you hire a therapist. If you have a professional contact, friend, and/or acquaintance you can learn from, ask them for help. Do not procrastinate! Take action intelligently and intentionally for the highest probability of full and comprehensive healing. If time allows and you are not in a crisis situation, read the Ethical Principles of Psychologists and Code of Conduct (APA) Standard 10: Therapy section[9] (please refer to the appendix for more details) to better understand what to expect as you begin your search for a therapist. It is cumber-

---

9. "Ethical Principles of Psychologists and Code of Conduct." N.p., n.d. Web. 07 Nov. 2016. www.apa.org/ethics/code/index.aspx.

some information, but if you are a research personality APA is a good place to learn.

Be Patient, But Persistent

It can be frustrating finding the correct fit, and it can take time. Be persistent! (If your child is in danger, go to the nearest emergency room and ask for help.)

As you learn your role in your child's therapy, surround yourself with positive support from the professionals you hire. You need to genuinely support and immensely trust your professional team, your child's doctors/therapist/psychiatrist, etc. And, to the best of their ability, the professionals need to become an advocate for your child as well as for you.

Seek a Therapist for Your Child

We recommend you pick up the phone and, on behalf of your child and family, find a licensed eating-disorder professional.

"Finding a therapist that is a good fit for the person struggling with an eating disorder is vital. In order to heal, one must feel that they can be vulnerable with their therapist, and they must feel that they can trust their therapist. There are all kinds of therapists, who operate from all kinds of philosophies and under a vast array of training. Sorting out who believes what can be daunting. As a therapist, who specializes in eating disorder recovery, I'd like to offer some suggestions.

1. We all have different areas of expertise and training. Eating disorder treatment is difficult. It requires specific supervision and experience. Many ethical therapists who do not have the skills to treat an eating disorder will refer you out to someone who specializes in this field. Others may decide to take on a client without necessarily having the capacity to do so skillfully. Please make sure your therapist has significant experience in treating eating disorders.

2. It is unethical for therapists to ask for testimonials from clients. If you are able to get a word-of-mouth referral from a friend, take it. Do not be alarmed if a therapist does not have a website or marketing materials, as it may indicate that their practice is fully based on word-of-mouth referrals.

3. Therapists are human beings. Some of us have done a significant amount of work in our own therapy, digging deeply into our own psyche and attempting to get an understanding of what we are bringing into the room as we work with clients. Others of us are less invested in working on ourselves, and more likely to have blind spots about what we are bringing into the therapeutic space. You should feel comfortable asking him or her about their relationship to their own bodies and to food. Some therapists are in recovery from eating disorders, and this is wonderful. Who better to help someone in the struggle than someone who has been

through it and has come out the other side successfully? However, other therapists may be avoidant of their own struggles, and could therefore become an obstacle to the recovery of clients. If you ask your therapist about their interest in working in this field and with this population, you should get a straightforward and direct answer.

4. *A good fit means just that: it's a fit. One therapist does not fit all. You may have to shop around to find a therapist that feels safe, present, engaging, and trustworthy to you and/or the client. If this takes time, the time is well spent. This will become a vital relationship and one of the key aspects of long-term recovery. Make sure that you find a therapist that creates an environment for the conditions of safety to be met."*

– Melody Moore, PhD, Licensed
Clinical Psychologist

If you do not know a therapist in your area, ask a friend or acquaintance for a recommendation. Ask your child's pediatrician for a referral. You can always tap into resources at your child's school. Talk with the school counselors, coaches, teachers, and/or the school nurse. If you have a primary-care physician ask him or her for a referral. If you are truly stumped and cannot find a therapist, search online. Here are three resources to consider:

- The National Eating Disorders Association's Helpline[10]
- Eating Disorder Hope[11]
- ED Referral[12]

> *Please refer to the appendix in the back*
> *of this book for more details.*

> *"I'll tell you what, I got to my goal weight, and I still wasn't satisfied. I had actually just internally sworn off bread as a "bad food." I was no longer "allowed to eat!" When my parents realized the extent of my struggle, they got me help. Without treatment, I would have continued to push my goal weight lower and lower, because it was "never good enough." There was always more weight to lose and more food groups to outlaw, in my disordered mind."*
> — From One Who is Grateful My Parents Stepped In

Consultation

If time allows, before hiring a therapist, set up an in-person consultation. Ask the therapist to meet with you (and/or you and your spouse/partner) first before your child sees him or her. You may need to interview with several professionals until you find

10. "Find Help & Support." National Eating Disorders Association. N.p., n.d. Web. 07 Nov. 2016. www.nationaleatingdisorders.org/find-help-support>.
11. "Eating Disorders Counselors, Therapists, Psychologists, Specialists Directory List." Eating Disorder Hope RSS. N.p., n.d. Web. 10 Nov. 2016. www.eatingdisorderhope.com/treatment-for-eating-disorders/therapists-specialists.
12. "Referral Request for Treatment Eating Disorders." Referral Request for Treatment Eating Disorders. N.p., n.d. Web. 10 Nov. 2016. www.edreferral.com.

your optimum match in a therapist, licensed professional, and/or psychiatrist. You want one who is well-versed in the field of eating disorders. Pick the one you feel is fundamentally best-suited for your child, you, and your family. Use your intuition. Your child needs to be invested in the therapist. If it is not a "match," move on. All good therapists understand that action.

If you have an adult child, you can be the catalyst, but they choose their own therapist. Most likely you will not be granted an in-person consultation unless your adult child agrees.

Questions We Suggest You Ask a Therapist

Ask the potential therapist questions in the consultation to better understand the reasons for therapy and the relationships to be developed between all parties. There are no wrong questions, and you should feel free to ask what you deem necessary. NEDA, National Eating Disorders Association's, "Parent Tool Kit"[13] is a great reference for questions. Please refer to the appendix in the back of the book for details and NEDA's suggestion questions.

Here are some additional questions we have found helpful in securing a therapist for your child:

- How long have you been treating eating disorders? Are you licensed, and if so, how?
- How long are your sessions? What is your fee? What is your availability?
- Do you work in tandem with my child's school/coaches, etc.?
- How do you handle insurance? If I don't have insurance coverage, do you offer scholarships? Do you have a slid-

---

13. "Parent Toolkit." National Eating Disorders Association. N.p., n.d. Web. 07 Nov. 2016. www.nationaleatingdisorders.org/parent-toolkit.

ing-fee scale?

- What are your fixed boundaries between the parents and you as a therapist? Will you communicate with us, and if so, what is your style and preference?
- If my child is over the age of eighteen, will you allow written consent from my child so I can communicate with you about his/her therapy?
- Do you offer family therapy? If not, whom do you recommend? What is your professional relationship with them?
- What do you need from us? Medical records/medical history?
- Do you prescribe medication? If so, we want to discuss before giving our child a prescription.
- Will you communicate regularly with other doctors on my child's treatment team?

Questions After You Have Hired a Therapist

After you have chosen the therapist who is the best fit for your child and family, continue to ask questions so that you fully understand the boundaries of that therapist's practice. Some therapists have conventional boundaries; other therapists have unconventional boundaries. Ask questions like:

- What role do I play and not play as a parent within your practice?
- What do you expect from me as the mother?
- Can I expect a call if my child is in danger and/or needs extra support?
- Can I call/text/email you my concerns? Will the call be kept confidential, or will you tell my child about our conversation?
- What are the "big picture" goals?

Parent-therapist Conferences

We recommend you commit to partake in parent-therapist conferences if your child is under the age of eighteen. (If your child is an "adult," he or she must sign a waiver to allow you communication with their therapist.)

Sample questions to ask the therapist:

- Will my child be involved, and/or is the conference confidential?
- Will the information shared in the conference be confidential, or do you feel it's important to tell our child about the conversation?
- Will you inform us if our child is in danger? Will you aide us in helping to prevent a potentially irrevocable decision?

Do Parents Partake in Regular Sessions with Their Child?

This question can only be answered by the therapist. Sometimes we get confused on what our parental role is in regards to our child and their therapist. We recommend you ask the therapist up front so you understand the connections or lack thereof. Each therapist/counselor has his or her own principals about parental involvement and communication, which are often set according to the age of the patient, diagnosis, and reasons for therapy. It can be comforting for a child to have a parent present during a session, and/or it can feel awkward, especially for teenagers. Find a therapist whose approach is accommodating, and remember to ask their level of disclosure. Trust is a critical component in the confidential space of a therapist office. If a therapist does choose to confide in you (and we recommend this open line of communication), you are responsible to respect and never abuse the information shared. It is to never be used against a child in any way. The goal of the therapist and the parent is the same: comprehensive healing. Individual therapy between your child and a therapist is different than family therapy (family therapy is usually the entire immediate family). Some therapists will see the parents first, then visit with the child, and finally have a session with the parents and their child. You will have to decide what works best for your child, your family, and you. If you want to be involved in your child's therapy, ask the therapist's opinion. Ask the therapist any questions you deem important, and then be open to their answers.

Share Important Information with the Therapist

Never hesitate to share information with your child's therapist that you deem critical and/or important to the well-being of your child. A therapist is better when they have knowledge of their client. Also, recognize and be respectful of the therapist's time. A text and/or email from you might be more appropriate than expecting regular phone conversations. Your child's therapist will read your text/email, and they may or may not reply depending on their philosophy of parent/therapist boundaries.

There is absolutely no shame in asking for help. We keep saying this over and over in this book because some of us wish we had trusted the therapist earlier. We cannot go back and change our course of actions, but we can recommend you take your child for help now. Hiring a therapist for your child just might be the new beginning of a relationship you desire with your child. The decision to take a child to a professional is not an easy commitment; therapeutic work is often difficult and time-consuming. But it is worth the time and effort. Every single person who has written in this book has asked for help and seen a professional.

"The struggle to find effective treatment for a child suffering from an emotional disorder is a journey unto itself. There is not a "one size fits all" solution and typically there is not a defined and smooth pathway that assures any of us successful "therapy" roads. What I have learned as a mother of a child who suffers from disorders that affect the presumptive "normal" teenage life is that you have to empower yourself to become an educated advocate for your child and put one foot in front of the other and get to it. We all have our own methodology of approaching the unknown. But, I believe the more we learn and educate ourselves as the parent then the more we can filter through for our child in advance so they may utilize their energies and emotions to get better. No one wants to sit back and watch their child suffer . . . but, sometimes the path to therapy can be so overwhelming as to who, what and when . . . that the winner is "indecision." And, then no one gets better. I highly recommend that parents «interview» a therapist first that they might be considering for their child without their child at the first consultation. This worked well for me as I wanted to ask the hard questions and it gave me a chance to get a feel for whether the therapist felt like a good fit for my child. Secondly, never feel that you cannot make a change if it's not clicking for your child. Developing a good relationship takes time, and everyone will need to be extremely patient; but, sometimes your intuition is the best guide and you must empower yourself to be the leader of your child's care. It's important to respect your child's opinions and feedback; but, also, it's important for them to experience progress. Above all . . . keep growing your heart bigger as you advocate for your child and although they

might not express to you in words how much your uncondi-tional love means to them just know that they feel it and need it every step of the way."
    — A Mom in the Fight on Behalf of Her Child

When is Enough, Enough?

The intention of therapy is to set the individual's needs in motion to learn coping skills, solve issues, and deal with problems that are blocking him or her from a full and healthy life. Eating disorders often require long-term therapy, and yet, there should be goals set from one milestone to the next. This takes time, but after three to six months, if you do not witness any change, consider hiring a new therapist. Progress in your loved one's therapy sessions is vital to their emotional health. Hopefully, after six to ten sessions you witness behavioral changes or better communication skills. If you feel like they are "stuck in reverse," consider a change. Ask your loved one if they feel like they are getting what they need out of therapy. If they say no, consider a change.

Remember that if your loved one is undernourished, they are incapable of thinking with a clear mind. Therapy is extremely helpful, but you have to be honest about the state of health your child is in. If they need hospitalization and/or full-time residential care, therapy is a waste of time and money. An experienced, reputable therapist will "graduate" their clients and even refer them elsewhere if the relationship is not a good fit.

"My niece is one of the most capable individuals I have ever met. She is very smart, driven and well spoken. And,

this is often the same description of girls with eating disorders. Well, aren't these the same girls who can change this world? Aren't these the people we want to run our companies and educate our kids?? Well, let's put them out there to do just that. Let them use therapy when necessary but don't leave them in therapy to talk about their problems forever. Let them use therapy then put them out there as a gift to others!"

— An Aunt

So what is the purpose of therapy? Over time, the work should help relieve pain, shame, and hurt, and ultimately help in your child's efforts to help themselves. A good therapist guides your child in learning important behavioral changes and effective habits and finding comfort in coping with feelings with the goal of living a more authentic life of purpose. Once honesty is established between your child and the therapist the hard work of discovery and recovery begins. Our hope for you is that with time, you will notice a happier child who is more insightful, less fearful, and more empowered in themselves, understanding they are uniquely and beautifully created. This discovery takes time. It is our deepest hope that, once again, you will feel a connection with your child and that he or she will open up to you and share their life with you and the family.

Does This Feel Familiar?

Please Help Me Out of This Hell!

"If you would have told me when I first started out on this journey that by the end

of it I would've been in therapy for seven years, seen over fifteen different doctors, and been to two different treatment centers . . . I would have called you crazy. You see, I didn't think that I had a problem, at least not one that I couldn't fix myself. I was a self-helper, a perfectionist, a grade A student. I didn't need some 'treatment' that was going to be a useless waste of money. I didn't need someone to tell me what I already knew. I was fine. Everything was fine. These are the lies that I lived in and went to bed with. They became so normal that I actually started to believe them. I convinced myself that my eating habits weren't 'that weird.' That my weight loss was 'not that bad.' And that my addiction to exercise was simply me being 'healthy.' Let me be clear here. If you want your loved one to have a chance at beating this thing we call an eating disorder, get them professional help now! It is the most powerful way you can love them, it is their best shot at full recovery, it is their hope. Do not overlook the struggle they are facing simply due to their ability to convince themselves that they are 'fine.' They are not. They need help. They need the help of a professional. This beast of a disorder cannot be fought alone. Your loved one is going to need the absolute BEST team of warriors possible, and trust me, you want the warriors to be ones with experience in the field. Help them build that team of warriors . . . and by doing that, you are actually fighting alongside them as well. I needed my team. I needed them to fight with me for years. It took me a long time to unravel the causes, triggers, and nuances of what fueled my disorder. It required really painful and really hard work and the willingness of my professional team to help guide me towards a healthy and happy life that I wanted to be living. My doctors and therapists saved my life. Without the treatment, without the professional help I would likely be dead. Thank God my parents knew the crucial need for this type of care and were able to get me into the right hands at the right time. My plea would be that you would not wait for your loved one to get any further into the depths their struggle. Help them begin the climb out of their hell into recovery now by getting them to the warriors who can help them to fight with all of their might for the life that your loved one deserves!"

– An Advocate and Recovered Healthy Woman

8 GET PROFESSIONAL HELP FOR YOURSELF, NOW

[
You can't help them if you don't help yourself!
It's courageous to seek help.
]

First and foremost, we believe a person can recover from an eating disorder, and we know the "therapeutic work" is worth the effort. Recovery is about discovering the authentic human being you were uniquely created to be by learning to love yourself, and thus, love others. This discovery is about you as well as your child. Don't we all want to be happy with who we are and who we are becoming as a person? Therapy can help you discover, re-create, develop, and mature certain aspects of your nature and character.

As moms we tend to give all our attention to our kids and often deprive ourselves of the exact processing we are asking of our children!

"For ten years, I was so consumed by the state of my daughter's eating disorder, 80 percent of my focus was on it—not myself, my husband, my other children nor my friends. It

was not until the joy I felt with the birth of my first grand-child that I realized what I had missed out on. I was phys-ically present at the important events with my family, but I wasn't emotionally invested, due to the worry of my sick daughter. How sad to waste so much energy on something I loathed and had no control over. Take care of yourself and your loved ones. It's important for them to see that the eating disorder is not going to take you down as well. It's a destruc-tive behavior that just gives ED more power."

— A Mother and Grandmother

There are benefits in going through therapy at the same time as your child. It provides a common thread and helps you become a relational human being with your child. Sometimes we need to know ourselves better in order to be what our child desires us to be and what we aspire to be. The common thread is about rela-tionship.

Too many people who refuse therapy say things like: "I don't need it," "It's weak to have to get outside help," "They don't know me and can't understand," "It's too expensive," "Of course a therapist wants to help because that's how they make money," and "I don't have time!"

The list is endless.

It is sad because that kind of self-pride stagnates healing both for the child and for the adult.

There is a responsibility as a parent to be the adult in the re-lationship. If you need to learn coping skills, then you must move forward in getting help. It is stubborn, prideful, and irresponsible not to seek help in educating yourself on how to communicate and tap into your child's psyche. Your child does not have a fully matured brain—you do. With that said, do not expect your child to change if you are not willing to lead the way in making the necessary changes in your mental health and, in turn, the family dynamics.

We as moms and caretakers have to try to remember it is not just about us. We often personalize our child's struggle, and it can become about us, not them. Try to listen open-mindedly, learn and discover both the positive assets of yourself, and take on the responsibilities of strengthening others. Remember, we are exquisitely human, and that means that we are nowhere near perfect. Often the ones who refuse therapy are the ones who need it most. There is a wide range of favorable treatments used to heal. Yes, some therapeutic help is very expensive, and others are free. We highly recommend you find the right fit for you.

Afraid to open Pandora's box? Scared of being different? Scared of being the same? Understandable. But, if your child is willing to try, you should be too. If you are open to learning, there is a tremendous upside.

What Could a Mom Do Now?

Secure professional help for yourself and educate yourself in these four areas: personal therapy, marriage/partner/couple counseling, family therapy, and self-help therapy. Below are five thoughts to consider.

Ask for Referrals

Word-of-mouth referrals seem to work the best. If you know someone who has dealt with and/or is dealing with this issue, call and ask them for help. If not, get a referral from your child's therapist, your primary-care physician, friends, acquaintances, colleagues, or family members.

If you are truly stumped and cannot find a therapist, please see the appendix in the back of this book for referrals from NEDA[14], The National Eating Disorder Association,[15] and/or IAEDP, and ED Referral.[16]

Secure a Personal Therapist

Your personal therapist should educate you on the disease as well as open your heart and mind to proficient tools that are helpful in both your personal life and parenting style. We recommend you find a licensed therapist who is trained in eating disorders because:

- They are specific to the knowledge and updated on the newest issues with eating disorders.
- They are trained in the field of eating disorders and know how to deal with the emotional issues that lie beneath the surface.
- They are trained in co-existing illness.
- They are connected to other professionals whose involvement will benefit your child's healing such as: licensed dieticians, medical doctors, family therapists, local school counselors, current workshops, retreats, etc.

Engage in Marriage/Couple Counseling

Many of us have opted for marriage counseling during the years we dealt with our child's/loved one's eating disorder. Some of

14. "Find Treatment." National Eating Disorders Association. N.p., n.d. Web. 10 Nov. 2016. www.nationaleatingdisorders.org/find-treatment.
15. "Find Treatment." National Eating Disorders Association. N.p., n.d. Web. 10 Nov. 2016. www.nationaleatingdisorders.org/find-treatment.
16. "Referral Request for Treatment Eating Disorders." Referral Request for Treatment Eating Disorders. N.p., n.d. Web. 10 Nov. 2016. www.edreferral.com

us are not married or in a committed relationship, so individual therapy was sufficient.

We all have our strengths and weaknesses, and learning how to communicate more clearly and understand each other's feelings/positions helped define appropriate actions we needed to take in our family. It is essential to the longevity of recovery to understand your spouse/life partner as soon as possible and for you to become a team. There are also times that only you can decide what must happen in your marriage/relationship with regards to not only the destructive eating disorder, but also your life.

There are couples fulfilled by doing therapy sessions together and do not want individual therapy. Some people prefer to start with personal one-on-one time with a therapist. It can help ground you, especially if you are new to therapy, just starting the journey, and/or in conflict with your spouse and need advice on how to communicate with them fairly. Again, reach out and ask for referrals.

For others, couple's counseling works best. If you are currently seeing a personal therapist, ask them if marriage/couple counseling is appropriate. If so, ask them for a referral. You will need to make that personal decision as to what serves you best—personal therapy or couple's therapy—at this particular time in your life.

Engage in Family Therapy

Ask your personal therapist if they will lead family therapy for your immediate family members. If not, ask for a referral who they are comfortable working with. For many of us, family therapy has been extremely beneficial especially when additional children are involved. An eating disorder never affects just one member of a family. It is a problem for every member of the family that needs to be addressed and dealt with together.

There are two incredibly important aspects of family therapy. First, everyone learns coping skills both for themselves and skills on how to deal with the disease. Secondly, even if family therapy is painful, learning to communicate, listen, respect, and respond thoughtfully is healthy for the family unit.

> *"Family therapy allows everyone to be heard, from the pain and despair of the parents, to the fear and anger of the siblings. The entire family is affected and each one needs to know that they can contribute to the recovery of their loved ones. Family therapy helps us understand our roles, and in some cases defines triggers that we may not be aware of. Through therapy we can learn how to make the changes for a healthier, more supportive environment. And equally important, standing strong on a unified front with your family and holding the eating disordered accountable for their actions gives the illness less control and power. Commitment and determination from every member of the family will help save your loved one's life."*
>
> – A Mom Who Knows That Every Voice
> in Her Family is Important

Engage in Self-help Therapy

By "self-help," we are referring to getting an education from others and/or accessing more affordable and/or free information. It is wise to learn from others who have "been there, done that." We realize caretaking a loved one battling an eating disorder is expensive, yet be careful—there is misguiding and false information on the internet. And there are so many opinions it is can be completely overwhelming! If you cannot afford therapy, below are two self-help resources. (Please see the appendix in the back of the book for more information on these two self-help resources.)

1. Parents Supporting Parents "Around the Dinner Table" is an online community of parents from all around the world. We recommend this because you can have a live conversation with other parents.[17]

2. Abigail Nathenshon's workbook, *When your Child has an Eating Disorder, a Step-by-Step Workbook for Parents and Caregivers*,[18] is thorough, educational, and self-paced.

A good therapist is a non-objective third party who non-emotionally helps you dissect and restructure issues that are currently destructive. He/she is on your team as an advocate who helps you think, decipher, and negotiate new beginnings. Think of it as continuing education. Learning more about who you are helps you direct your way in the world. It also helps you become a better parent.

Destroying the false image of supermoms and perfectionists and surrendering to the fact that we can't do it all opens us up to the relationships we yearn for with our loved one: honest, real, respectful, and authentic. This may take some humility.

Therapy looks different for each individual/family as it is tailored to specific needs. Are there any areas in your life where you feel confused, inadequate, or simply need a more thorough education? Could you and your family use some professional help learning to communicate more candidly without the discomfort

17. "ATDT Home Page." F.E.A.S.T. N.p., n.d. Web. 07 Nov. 2016. www.aroundthedinnertable.org.
18. Nathenshon Abigail H. Natenshon (Author), Abigail. When Your Child Has an Eating Disorder: A Step-by-Step Workbook for Parents and Other Caregivers 1st Edition. Jossey-Bass. New York. 1999. Print.

of being misunderstood? Is your child shut down and not sharing their self with you? Therapy could be the perfect catharsis that you and your family need in order to strengthen and grow.

Does This Feel Familiar?

If My Pain Can Help Just One Family

"It's hard for me to try to go back and relive that day. But if my thoughts and memories can help just one family, I'll take the road back in my mind, no doubt. So . . . does this feel familiar?

The morning we left our daughter at the hospital, I felt like my world had fallen through a giant, deep, dark hole in the ground. The excruciating guilt pulling me down while questioning myself, "Did I let my precious child get sick?" I remember being in a fetal position on the floor in our family den when my parents walked through the front door. Not knowing which way was up, I was able to eek out that my husband and I had left her at treatment without her blessing. It was torture. All I knew was that my girl—the precious child I have been bonded to for seventeen years—was in the hospital fighting an eating disorder and I wasn't with her. If not for my God, friends who'd experienced similar things, and our family, this mama might not have made it through.

I know now, and learned quickly while she was in treatment, that I didn't "let" her get sick . . . she just became sick. Her journey was slow at first and things did not seem abnormal but suddenly, that "seemingly normal" went downward in a spiral that I couldn't see coming, at least as fast as it did. She started to lose weight during her junior year in high school. We were concerned a little, but were quickly reassured (by her) that she was just trying to be healthy. Day after day, we saw slow changes. We had noticed her getting thinner and her eating habits were signaling a problem. For instance, she would eat smaller amounts and eat the SAME thing every day. I'm guessing this is so she knew how many calories she was consuming without having to calculate differently each day. Another important clue was, whenever she got home, she would turn on the gas fireplace and sit on the hearth to warm up. She had no body fat, so was cold all the time. Interestingly enough, her behavior was pretty much the same! She was sweet and happy like normal. I think if her personality had changed in some way, we would have been more on top of things and investigated earlier.

Cut to the chase, she was admitted to the hospital as a day patient for six weeks. She hated it. So with the hate that came from being there, she was able to create a drive and determination like nothing I have ever seen. The doctors and nurses and aides stuck with her and she with them and her mind began to change.

We have been asked many times, how we got through it. Like I said earlier, we could not have persevered without God, family and friends. I've learned a lot and know for sure that I never want to go through something of this caliber without a wingman. My wingman during this family challenge was my dear husband. He was present, listened and loved throughout it all. He might not have known exactly what do at times, but just BEING there, was most important. He is much more practical than I, so he talked me off the edge more than once. He was amazing. A wingman doesn't have to be a husband, just someone near and dear that you can communicate with . . . be it praying with, gushing to, venting to, crying and/or laughing with, you just need a wingman. All of this being said, it was our strong little girl, most of all, who was the champion. She WANTED to get better and did. Although she hated treatment, she made a choice to listen to her team of doctors and apply the knowledge daily. She liked her doctors and had utmost respect for them, but in order to get her on the right track, they had to watch her with eagle eyes. That would be hard for anyone. She knew they were doing their job, but she didn't like being the subject of their interests. Just having someone observe each meal and each trip to the bathroom—it was overwhelming. She found an aide that she really bonded with which made it easier to go to treatment each day. She felt as if someone really cared and understood, more like a friend than a doctor. In all our years together as a family, I've never been more proud of her and her willingness to give full reign to someone else. She made the decision to give up control to allow the team at the hospital to redirect her mind to a healthy, no-ED place. Getting better was her number one goal.

There's a saying: "CHOOSE JOY." It's not that easy for some, and I totally get that. However, in our circumstance, this was our only option. It helps that I was raised by two amazingly loving and joyful parents who taught by example. I watched how they navigated life's ups, downs, disappointments and thrills. I learned all I know about love and joy, from them. I am blessed. So each morning on the thirty-minute drive to the hospital, my daughter and I CHOSE joy. It did not mean it was easy but it helped make it bearable. It was our only option. We sang, prayed and even laughed some. It might have been a nervous laugh, but we consciously chose joy in the blessing of recovery.

God is so good. We got through it. She got through it and is better than ever.

My ultimate hope and prayer is that both my daughter and I, at some point in time, will be able to help someone in crisis, just as we were helped."

— A Loving Mom Who Fought for Her Child's Freedom

9 REGISTERED DIETICIANS AND NUTRITIONISTS

[
Nutrition is critical to the chemistry of the brain. Without proper nutrition, brain chemistry is altered and does not perform in its optimal range.
]

Lack of nutrition can decelerate thoughts, causing both physical and emotional dysmorphia. Dysmorphia is when a person sees and feels abnormalities that are not real except to them.[19] For example, have you heard your underweight child say, "I feel fat?" It makes no sense in your mind but, due to lack of nutrition, the mind of someone struggling with anorexia literally sees his or her body different than the physical reality. The grip of an eating disorder is much more prevalent when the mind and body are malnourished.

For those suffering from anorexia, a starved brain makes it difficult to engage in therapy, so nutritional weight restoration is critical to the recovery process. With this said, a dietician and/or nutritionist is an important part to the success of the treatment team.

---

19. *Mayo Clinic.* "Body Dysmorphic Disorder." Overview. N.p., 28 Apr. 2016. Web. 07 Nov. 2016. www.mayoclinic.org/diseases-conditions/body-dysmorphic-disorder/home/ovc-20200935.

Sadly, we have seen a substantial amount of harm caused by alleged dieticians/nutritionists who do not have the expertise in eating disorders. An exorbitant amount of time is wasted unwinding the misguided information. For example, calorie counting is a negative learned behavior. Today, there are many dieticians/nutritionists who do not ask their clients to keep account of their caloric intake. Once a person masters calorie-counting they cannot reverse the issue later in life. Like unwinding your ABCs or simple math, 2+2=4, it is impossible to unlearn the patterns. That is only one example of why it is critical to hire a licensed eating-disorder dietician and/or nutritionist who is experienced.

> *"I have this story in my head, a script of how it's "supposed" to be. Filtered, edited, revised, and photoshopped—producing the ideal image of me. I have this story in my head of how I ought to look. A Barbie image, objectified to the media's perfect picture from a never-ending book of rules . . . of rules, regulations, and policies to follow. Teaching me that if I do not fit into their definition I am nothing else but unlovable. So bleeding, aching, hurting, I strive to stand up to this perfection. Allowing myself, my body, my appearance to become my one obsession."*
> – Former Victim of an Eating Disorder

What Could a Mom Do Now?

Focus on the big-picture goal of your child's freedom. Visualize them cured of negative and distorted thoughts about food and themselves. Support your child's efforts to normalize their eating and learn to listen and trust their body's internal hunger cues. The ultimate goal is intuitive social eating. Sharing meals is a social and bonding activity in all cultures. Therefore, choose a dietician and/or nutritionist who knows that eating is not just about food.

There is no such thing as perfection when it comes to eating and food choices. Every single culture has their rituals around eating, specific foods that are preferred, and traditional foods for celebrations. Many people have peculiar food habits; some are vegetarians, gluten-free, or non-dairy. And though the habits are odd or choices narrow, they do not have an eating disorder that constantly interrogates their thoughts, projecting negativity, self-hatred, and shame. There is a difference—a difference so vast that the mental illness/eating disorder is actually trying to kill in the form of a slow suicide. Though that sounds harsh, it is true. An eating disorder is a mental illness that controls the mind, behaviors, and perspectives. Comprehensive healing is when the eating disorder no longer controls a person's thoughts. There are no more hateful thoughts discrediting their existence. It truly is not just about the food; at first the intake of food is critical to restore health. Learning to be comfortable with and around food is also critical and a difficult step for many people struggling with an eating disorder. Comprehensive healing is about alleviating the mental illness that constantly degrades, humiliates, and finally convinces people they are not worthy of living.

It is important that you engage a dietician/nutritionist who understands eating disorders because there are consequences to what your child and/or loved one learns. Please hire an accredited and qualified dietician/nutritionist. Below are eight things to consider to help you move forward when hiring a dietician or nutritionist. (Note: if your loved one is in a treatment center they will be assigned to a staff dietician/nutritionist.

The Options and Differences Between Dieticians and Nutritionists

Dieticians and nutritionists should always be part of a multi-disciplinary team including physicians, psychiatrists, and therapists. It is considered unethical if one is the only health professional treating a patient with an eating disorder. The different titles, certifications, and acronyms change with new development in the field and can be a bit confusing if you are just starting this journey of seeking help. Find someone both you and your child jell with. If your loved one is over eighteen years old, helping them find a satisfactory fit is wonderful, but ultimately they get to choose. The relationship should always be professional. Though you always have to trust your doctors, forming a friendship is usually not the case. Please be cognitive of choosing a person who is well-trained because a non-accredited/non-licensed individual can unintentionally harm the psyche of a person struggling with negative body image. Time, training, and knowledge will give way to new and various titles for dieticians and nutritionists. Please do additional research until you feel informed.

"A friend suggested I take my athletic child to a 'nutritionist.' Naively I did, and within twenty minutes of conversation the nutritionist had suggested my child was too heavy and her BMI was unhealthy. What my daughter heard was, 'You are fat!' She was only twelve years old. It was the final tipping point and she began to starve herself. It took her almost eight years to get beyond anorexia and the self-loathing feeling of 'I am fat.' So sad." If only I had known."

– A Once-naïve Mom

Registered Dieticians/Registered Dietitian Nutritionists have completed rigorous academic and experiential prerequisites required by ACEND, Accreditation Council for Education in Nutrition and Dietetics. A registered dietician is referred to as an RD and/or a Registered Dietitian Nutritionist, RDN. A RD/RDN is a specialist who has expertise in nutrition, foods, nourishment, the effects on the body, and the science of nutrition. Many of us who have written in this book have been happy with RD/RDNs, most especially when they are experienced with eating disorders. These professionals have met all national/international legal standards, completed an accredited internship, passed the registration exam, are registered, licensed, and legally protected, carry the professional title RD/RDN, and are required to maintain their educational requirements.[20]

Nutritionists have varying definitions. Unlike a RD/RDN, the law does not protect the title "nutritionist." Individuals who refer to themselves as nutritionists may or may not have nutritional education and/or a four-year bachelor's degree in nutrition and/or a master's degree to operate as a nutritionist. Not all nutritionists are dieticians, so be careful when choosing a qualified professional.[21]

A Certified Nutrition Specialist (CNS) is an accredited nutrition expert who must complete a master's degree or doctoral degree, complete a hundred hours of supervised experience, pass the certification exam, and maintain their certification by continuing professional education. If you choose to hire a nutritionist please ask about their experience with eating disorders and pro-

20. "Accredited and Approved Dietetics Education Programs – Accreditation Council for Education in Nutrition and Dietetics – from the Academy." *Accredited and Approved Dietetics Education Programs – Accreditation Council for Education in Nutrition and Dietetics – from the Academy*. N.p., n.d. Web. 08 Nov. 2016. www.eatrightacend.org/ACEND/content.aspx?id=6442485414.
21. "About ASCEND." N.p., n.d. Web. 08 Nov. 2016. www.eatrightacend.org.

fessional education.[22]

A Holistic Nutritionist promotes an integrative approach to eating by emphasizing optimal health for mind, body, and soul. There are several educationally proficient holistic nutritionist programs. Holistic nutrition seems to have a bright and promising future as an emerging field, yet many states do not regulate the use of this title. Again, if you choose to go the holistic route, please make sure the individual is experienced in eating disorders.

> *"Holistic nutrition is the modern natural approach to developing a healthy balanced diet while taking into account the person as a whole. Holistic nutrition is considered to be part of holistic health. Food not only provides the energy needed to function in our daily lives but constantly supplies the nutrients which are required to build and regenerate body tissue, bone, muscle, fat and blood. The nutrients in food are also necessary to produce substances for the chemical processes that take place in our bodies millions of times a day."[23]*
>
> – HolisticNutrition.com

Naturopaths are licensed Doctors of Naturopathic Medicine (ND, NMD) and have completed a four-year, graduate-level program accredited by the Council on Naturopathic Medical Edu-

---

22. "The Certified Nutrition Specialist® (CNS®) Credential." BCNS. N.p., n.d. Web. 08 Nov. 2016. www. nutritionspecialists.org/cns/certified-nutrition-specialists.
23. "Holistic Nutrition." Holistic Nutrition.com. N.p., n.d. Web. 08 Nov. 2016. www.holisticnutrition.com.

cation.[24] They are very well-educated as the first two years of a naturopathic medical degree are the same as for traditional medical students. Naturopathic doctors take a holistic approach when possible, and yet, most NDs are willing to work in conjunction with Medical Doctors (MD). Licensed Naturopaths can assess your child scientifically (through blood work) and deal naturally with the imbalances in the brain and body through science. They are also seen as nutritionists and educators on the subject of health. (Please refer to the "Innovative Treatments and Therapies" section of the book for more information.)

Nutritional Therapists are popular and individualized. A registered nutritional therapist desires to administer the right foods and/or nutrients to link physical and mental health. Nutritional therapists attempt to rehabilitate behavior regarding food in hopes of stabilizing, and eventually normalizing, a client's eating pattern, but it is not the same as nutrition counseling. When dealing with eating disorders, most nutritional therapy is overseen by a Registered Dietician (RD).[25]

Beware! Traditional Eating Disorder Dieticians and/or Nutritionist are specialists who meet with the client and devise a structured plan to monitor food intake with "food logs" while sticking to a certain meal plan with caloric boundaries. Asking a patient to count calories in an attempt to get enough nutrition in for the day is a dangerous and a very slippery slope, especially for teens. Once a person starts monitoring food by keeping count of calories they cannot unwind the knowledge of numbers. We believe counting calories keeps a child in his or her eating-disorder mindset. It be-

24. "Council on Naturopathic Medical Education." *Council on Naturopathic Medical Education.* N.p., n.d. Web. 08 Nov. 2016. www.cnme.org/>.

25. "What Is a Registered Dietitian Nutritionist?" *Www.eatrightpro.org.* N.p., n.d. Web. 08 Nov. 2016. www.eatrightpro.org/resources/about-us/what-is-an-rdn-and-dtr/what-is-a-registered-dietitian-nutritionist>.

comes an obsession and makes comfortable intuitive social eating much more difficult to reach. We absolutely do not endorse calorie-counting.

Having said that, here are more controversial, yet common, methods we recommend you avoid:

- Calorie-counting (You cannot unlearn once learned.)
- Weighing clients (The number on the scale can keep a person in his or her eating disorder.)
- Body Mass Index (BMI): This is not measurable for everyone on the charts, and some people do not fit the "averages."
- Low weight acceptance
- Stigma of "being in shape"
- Eating only "healthy" foods: Restricting the diet to only so-called "healthy foods" can be confusing for someone struggling with an eating disorder. Of course, eating healthily is important, but an anorexic intentionally (or unintentionally) can abuse this notion.

Get a Referral

A referral from a friend or acquaintance who has hands-on experience with a specific dietician/nutritionist is the best way to move forward. You might also check with any doctors or therapists with whom you are currently involved, such as your child's school counselor, school nurse, the local health clinic, or college advisor.

If you do not have access to a referral, please do some research online. Try searching the International Federation of Eating Disorder Dieticians[26] and Eating Disorder Hope.[27] For more

---

26. "Find an Eating Disorder Dietician." Find an Eating Disorder Dietician. N.p., n.d. Web. 10 Nov. 2016. www.eddietitians.com.
27. "Eating Disorders Treatment." Eating Disorder Hope RSS. N.p., n.d. Web. 10 Nov. 2016. www.eatingdisorderhope.com.

details about these two organizations please refer to the appendix in the back of this book.

Consult with Your Child's Therapist/Doctor About Who to Hire

If your child is currently in therapy, ask the therapist who they recommend as a dietician/nutritionist and/or if they are familiar with the person you have hired. It is imperative they work together. Your therapist takes the lead in helping put the treatment team together. Your child's therapist and dietician/nutritionist are most constructive when working together and both communicating with you. It is unethical for a dietician/nutritionist to work solo with an eating disorder client.

Ask the therapist's thoughts and recommendations on licensed dieticians, holistic nutritionists, traditional eating-disorder dieticians/nutritionists, naturopaths, and nutrition therapy. If they are not well-versed in the answer, ask them for a referral to speak to someone who is experienced.

Ask the Potential Dietician/Nutritionist Questions

If possible, set up a consultation with the dietician/nutritionist before you hire them and before they meet with your child. Ask questions like:

- How much does a session cost?
- Do you take insurance?
- Are you licensed? If so, what is your education?
- What is your experience with eating disorders?
- Will you communicate with me? How often? With my child's therapist? How often?
- Can I contact you, and should I expect a return response?

- What are the boundaries between us?
- If my child is eighteen years of age or older, what is to be expected of me as the mom? Will you still communicate with me?
- Do you weigh your clients? How often and why?
- Do you measure BMI? Why and/or why not?
- Will you grocery shop with my child and/or share a meal? (Some dieticians will shop for food and help prepare and eat meals with patients and sometimes their families. We have found this to be very helpful.)
- What is your opinion on traditional eating-disorder dieticians/nutritionists—in particular their practice of things like calorie-counting and/or keeping food logs? (Just a reminder: we do not recommend these traditional methods.)
- Are there any new and innovative treatments you apply that have been successful?

Understand Re-feeding

Re-feeding is the act of reintroducing nutrition/food to patients who are severely malnourished. Re-feeding is most common in the treatment of anorexia and/or with a person who suffers from a severe medical issue. It seems easy enough to say, "Just eat!" but re-feeding is a serious and methodical process that should be monitored under the care of a doctor. If not done slowly and monitored correctly, complications occur such as "re-feeding syndrome." When starving, the body is in a catabolic state breaking down tissue for nutrients. Once an individual begins eating again, the body shifts to an anabolic state of rebuilding. Due to the change in metabolism, and because the body is hungry, a release of hormones occurs that can cause severe imbalances and complications. If your loved one is severely starved, take them to a hospital or treatment facility.

We highly recommend you work with an accredited dietician/ nutritionist who understands eating disorders and re-feeding.

If your loved one is currently in treatment, the treatment team will know how to handle this issue. Let them do their job; re-feeding a body is an intricate balance. As a mom or caretaker, this is a good time to learn and be educated. It is also the time to be the most loving advocate possible. Re-feeding is very emotionally hard for those suffering from anorexia or starvation; your children will need your support.

Understand Intuitive and "Social" Eating

The ultimate dream of health regarding nutrition is intuitive "social" eating, and sometimes freedom must be allowed for managing. Remember, eating disorders are about underlying emotional issues; it is not just about the food. Intuitive eating is about becoming both familiar and in tune with natural hunger signals. We also include the word social because eating comfortably with others is essential to the balance of life. When it is achieved, intuitive eating becomes an effective way of maintaining healthy weight, rather than keeping track of the amount of calories. It also feels more normal in the social bonding that occurs when eating with others, which is very important for the rest of a person's life.

In the book, *Intuitive Eating: A Revolutionary Program That Works*, doctors Evelyn Tribole and Elyse Resch give the reader a complete understanding of intuitive eating.[28] They reference ten principles of intuitive eating:

1. Reject the Diet

---

28. Tribole, Evelyn, and Elyse Resch. *Intuitive Eating: A Revolutionary Program That Works*. New York: St. Martin's Griffin, 2003. Print.

2. Honor Your Hunger

3. Make Peace with Food

4. Challenge the Food Police

5. Respect Your Fullness

6. Discover the Satisfaction Factor

7. Honor Your Feelings Without Using Food

8. Respect Your Body

9. Exercise—Feel the Difference

10. Honor Your Health

Learning how to train the brain and think positively about food helps us to use food to both nurture and satisfy the body without fear or false hope.

On more information on Intuitive Eating: A Revolutionary Program That Works *please refer to the appendix in the back of the book.*

Make a Change if Necessary

Remember, you are the mom or guardian and an important advocate for your child. If the relationship with the dietician/nutritionist is not compatible for your child, make a change. Personalities often play a part in the success and potential failure of the work. If you feel the need to employ a different professional, consult with your child's therapist/doctor and ask for a new referral.

Not Sure if You Can Afford a Dietician and/or Nutritionist?

Dieticians and nutritional therapies can be very expensive. If you are insured, ask your provider what they reimburse. (Please refer to chapter 12.)

If you are currently tight on money, and this component is not in the budget:

- Ask the other doctors on the treatment team for help.
- Look for scholarship opportunities.
- Negotiate pricing with the professional and ask for a sliding scale.
- Consult with a NEDA Navigator associated with the National Eating Disorder Association. These are trained volunteers with first-hand knowledge and experience with eating disorders. Ask for advice and help.

> *For more information on how to connect with a NEDA Navigator, please refer to the appendix in the back of this book.*

"Registered dieticians," "nutritionist," and "eating" are pretty sticky subjects with a variety of options. By no means are we being negative about the extremely important work of these skilled professionals, but once again, trust your intuition and make the best decision you can on behalf of your child, family, and yourself. You want a dietician/nutritionist who helps alleviate the burden of your constantly monitoring food intake. It is best to be led by the professional. Let them do their job so you can be a mom!

The value of the work can be found in the practical balance of mind, self, and food!

Does This Feel Familiar?

My Precious Twin, Lost to an ED

"The love my sister and I shared was deep, constant and unconditional. We were soul mates. We were identical twins. We often knew each other's thoughts and feelings without speaking. My sister was energetic, outgoing, positive and

caring. She made you feel important and special.

Both type A "pleasers" and achievers, my twin sister and I did not really "do conflict" well. Instead of voicing our negative feeling, we got busier. For my sister, after I made cheerleader and she didn't, I believe was when she clearly began to feel "less popular," "less loved" than me. My sister was always a little stronger athlete, a little higher in her grades, yet she never felt the approval of others like she needed. She saw herself as very capable but not necessarily "liked as well" or "as attractive to boys/men." Ironically, she was very well liked. Everyone loved my sister. She was elected class president, "best pledge" in her sorority at college and Phi Beta Kappa. These were all things she could "achieve" even "control" per se. Yet, they were not enough to validate her.

As we grew into young adulthood, she would say that her real "issue" that caused the eating disorder (which I will now refer to as "ED") was her relationship with our mother and mom's disapproval of her first husband. But in reality, her addiction started to manifest itself in college, years before that. There can be a "blame game" that goes on for ED patients. Perhaps it is easier to cast blame on others or circumstances rather than own up to the fact that a desperate desire to get what they want (maybe passive aggressive) or "control" their lives is the real issue. When I think back on my sister's relationships, the ones that were the most painful for her were the ones she could not control or change. Her relationship with her ED was one she could control or be in charge of. It was empowering. Until, the eating disorder took control of her.

She married and had children but, sadly, she could never seem to let go of ED. And for women with children, the color issues of ED can be transferred onto the children. She would want desperately to control their food, their decisions, etc. Her children have never known a well mom. They heard time after time "mommy is going away to get well." She would come home from treatment centers not well, then go again to "get well." The ED also became a type of parent in a way. IT decided on where they would go, when they would go, with whom they would go . . . until finally my sister went nowhere choosing to stay home with her lover ED instead of engaging in relationships with others. As her health worsened and her ED worsened her relationships with her husband and boys worsened. This caused more guilt and shame and self-loathing. My "normal" for over half of her and my life was not only helping her, but also helping her boys and being the go-between for her and her ex-husband. This too probably added to her feeling incapable. But it was my sister, the twin I so dearly loved, the other part of me and I would go to extreme measure to try to help her. That is what twins do.

I resented her illness and hated her ED. I raged at how it had stolen my sister, her boy's mother, my parent's daughter, her friendships. Everything was stolen by her secret lover. I felt guilt at my anger. Shouldn't I be more compassionate, more supportive? As my husband or others offered advice, I was angry with them. How could they understand? I became distant, closed off, tired, sad. I even developed a huge fear when I became pregnant with my second set of twins (identical girls like us!). I thought that part of the cause of my sister's ED was being constantly compared as an identical twin. I just knew that one of our girls would develop an ED. I had to seek the healing of the Lord big-time on this one! Fortunately, my sister's struggles became an opportunity to talk to our four girls and one son about eating disorders and addictions. And my husband and I really made an effort to encourage our twins to find their own identities and see who they are in their Lord, not who they are in the world's eyes or measurements.

As the ED became more severe, and she tried to fight it, she turned to another addiction—alcohol—and cast blame on it for her problems. I don't really remember when she started going to AA meetings, but I do know that she went to two treatment centers for "alcoholism." They both sent her home saying that they could not treat her because her primary addiction was the eating disorder. I believe she used the alcoholism as a red herring, so she would not have to address the ED. Yes, she wanted to get well, and she craved community. Alcoholism is accepted, even worn as a badge sometimes in our society. People readily tell us they are "off to their AA meetings." But this is NOT so with an eating disorder. It is a shameful disease; one we do not like to share or talk about. It is ugly, frightening, confusing. There are no "12 steps" to recovery! As my sister bought into AA, it took a seat out in the open, next to her secret lover. She would easily talk about her struggles with alcohol. It became a way of keeping me at a distance from her ED. She blamed all her issues on alcoholism. This infuriated me. I found myself resentful of AA, and even of her AA friends. I thought, "those people are so naïve to not see that her biggest problem is her ED!" So I came to a point where I couldn't stand it! I confronted her and told her that I knew that her ED was the root issue and that I did not want to hear any more about her alcoholism or AA. It was setting a boundary, hoping that this may encourage her to get more help for her ED. I wonder if this caused her more shame, more self-loathing, more disgust with herself at her allowing her ED to rule her life.

Towards the end, she was very self-focused. Almost like she had imploded. She was truly unable to believe that my life had challenges or pain. And let me assure you, though I feel very blessed, my life is not perfect. I am far from perfect. I do have a Type A personality. I like a routine. I like to feel in control. But I was never held hostage and I guess the difference is that I do love my blessed imperfect life and myself. I realized I did not have to be in control and through my Christian faith I was able to understand that my Lord didn't compare me or ask me to "earn" my worthiness. He simply asked me to trust Him and promised that even when life looks completely out of control, He is in control promising strength and growth and beauty out of life's messiness. My sister knew this, but I wish my sister had learned to surrender to this unequivocal power of God's mercy not to the power of ED.

Sadly, the lens she saw me through was so distorted that she began to only believe her "truths" rather than reality. I struggled with trying to explain my pains and challenges in order to show her that we ALL have issues hoping this would make her feel she wasn't alone in her pain. But I now think this may have instead made her feel unacknowledged or unheard which led to a feeling of unworthiness. I think this is why she was always drawn to people with many struggles, weak people, needy people, vulnerable people. She took on the pain of others in a (strange) way. As she did and could not "fix" them, she turned to her ED who would listen to her, comfort her, be waiting for her. This wrecks havoc on relationships and parenting! The ED became her secret lover.

She over the years spent more and more time with her ED and less and less time with others. This resulted in guilt and shame. Her dynamic, outgoing personality was overtaken by the protection of her secret shameful lover, the ED.

Although she distanced herself from family and social gatherings, we continued to talk daily. I went through a type of "survivor's guilt" as I watched the sister I knew and loved disappear. I thought, why her and not me? I often wondered what I could change to help her. I now realize that it was not me, or any of us that needed to change to help her as much as it was her perspective that needed to change. Yes, we need to be sensitive, encouraging, good listeners. But we also need to set boundaries, even do the hard thing, which can feel like the cruel thing.

At the end, ED won. The morning my sister died, I felt I "knew" when she slipped away. I had a strange peace sweep over me. I then received a call that she had died.

After her death, I realized I had spent over half of my life caring for her and her ED. I kept hearing from others "you will find your new normal." I continue to find my "new normal," but I do have peace. It is well with my soul. You see, I grieved my sister during the twenty-five years of her illness as she slipped away from me because of the ED. I know that now she is at peace—healed and whole—something she was not here on earth. This is what comforts me, that what carries me. The ED robbed us of so much, but it never stole our love."

– A Sister Who Lost Her Twin to an Eating Disorder

10 TREATMENT AND VARIOUS OPTIONS

[
Securing treatment and accepting help from professionals
reduces our burden and worry. We become more clear-minded
and powerful advocates.
]

How does a guardian know when it is time to move forward with treatment for their loved one? This is a difficult but defining question. First and foremost, if your child is in medical danger, take them to the nearest emergency ward. The staff there will walk you through the next steps and options regarding treatment.

Knowing the right moment to move forward with treatment is often complicated, not always a strategic plan, and sometimes a repetitive effort. When considering treatment, there are many variables to think about within the structure of the loved one's current lifestyle. You will know when the time is right, but that does not mean it will always be a smooth transition. Interrupting life for treatment is never a fun and exciting adventure, but it may be the deciding factor to saving your loved one's life. Always, and we mean always, the earlier you choose to address an eating disorder, the higher probability of restoring health.

So how will you know? Listen to your true internal voice that we call intuition. How do you really feel about the behavior and symptoms you are witnessing from your loved one? Are you in denial that there is a problem? Are they in denial? Are you making excuses for these new patterns of behavior, weight loss, or odd food habits? Are they making excuses for themselves? Very honestly, is there just something that is not right, but you can't put your finger on it? Do you know treatment is needed, but you are too intimidated, worried, or just downright scared to send your child away? If so, you are not alone. Many of us moms who have written in this book have had to send a child away for treatment. It was difficult. It was necessary.

"I went to a friend's office, who's firstborn child had battled an eating disorder in her teens, and through tears of fear and frustration I said, 'I do not know what to do.' My friend then explained the taxing days and nights of her worry and frustration fearful her child would never get past the eating disorder and die a pitiful death. She said they came to a crossroad and did not know what to do. They changed therapists four times and finally found a fit and a treatment center. They admitted their precious teenage child into full-time residential care at an eating disorder treatment center.

'It was against the will of my child who screamed, cried and begged me not to do this to her. We had to engage a social worker that came and physically took my child from our home. I wept, threw up and felt a physical pain that tore the heart right out of my chest.' But, as she went on to explain, 'Our decision saved her life.' Their child, now a healthy adult and mom herself, eventually thanked

her parents profusely for making her go to the treatment center. My friend still feels that pain and anguish from that day and was teary eyed reliving it in words. She went on to explained the tender heart of a mother and then she also explained there are times you have to guard your heart in a steal cage because you have to! Then my friend looked at me and said, "DO THE HARD THING. YOU HAVE TO DO THE HARD THING!"

– A Mom Who Did the Hard Thing and
Took Her Child to Treatment

What Could a Mom Do Now?

Let's begin with a general guide to standard types of treatment options. The options begin with critical condition treatment, to infrequent outpatient needs, then after-care. The name and definitions of treatment options vary with different eating-disorder consortiums, but here are the five basics:

- **Inpatient hospitalization.** The patient is critical enough to be hospitalized for medical stabilization. Restoring weight, dealing with medical complications from an eating disorder, and treating co-existing illnesses like depression and anxiety are common. The length of time is determined by the patient's progress, but on average is a two-to-four-weeks stay. Once stable they are released to a residential care program. When a patient is suicidal and/or in medical danger, take them to the nearest emergency room. The emergency room doctors and staff will stabilize the individual and offer treatment suggestions.

- **Residential care.** The patient is stable enough to live in a twenty-four-hour facility/residential care program and is not in an acute medical condition. All treatment, physical and psychological, is under one roof. A personalized treatment plan is created with a team consisting of (but not limited to) a psychiatrist, therapist, dietician, group therapy, and when ready, family therapy. A patient learns behavioral changes and coping skills. They deal with past trauma(s) and emotional pain, work to eat intuitively, identify triggers, and restore one's love of self and others. The patient works full-time in an effort to restore mental and physical health. The length of a stay is determined by both insurance and how the patient reacts to healing. It could be thirty days, or it could be two years. When people refer to a "treatment center," most often it is residential care.

- **Intensive Outpatient (IOP).** The patient is enrolled in a treatment facility or hospital setting but sleeps at home and/or where they are living. Most of the time, the patient maintains partial activities outside of treatment like limited school and/or work. Outpatient can be taxing on caregivers, but if sleeping at home stabilizes and feels safe, we recommend it, especially for younger children. The learned skill sets and treatment plans are similar to residential care but less restrictive. They meet in a group and are therapeutically led by a trained professional. The length of stay varies depending on the success and balance of daily living while positively contesting the negative eating-disorder behaviors. Individuals in IOP meet with the group one to four times a week for several hours at a time until released by their doctor.

Depending upon the age of the individual, parents most often participate in IOP. We suggest you get involved; it's a wonderful learning tool for you as well.

- **Outpatient.** Outpatient care is less frequent and a less restrictive level of treatment as the patient integrates back into daily life. The patient is medically and psychiatrically stable to function comfortably as they continue to make healthy decisions. The individual may still be a patient of the IOP team and/or engage individual licensed eating-disorder professionals such as an individual therapist and/or dietician.

- **Aftercare.** Before a patient is "discharged" from treatment, it is important to secure a nurturing aftercare scenario for maintaining support in hopes of successful long-term healing. Sometimes this is a plan put in place and loosely monitored by the treatment team, but it can also be an actual place of residence. Depending upon the age, the aftercare location may or may not be at home. Because relapse is a reality, an aftercare program feels essential for both accountability and productive healing. There is not a 100 percent guarantee that once your loved one goes to treatment they will overcome the eating disorder. Aftercare helps prevent relapse.

"Unfortunately, it's the curve balls in life that continue to bring our daughter back into a terrifying, unhealthy state. Whether it be the loss of a loved one, anxiety over a new job, transition into new living conditions, some of these major changes in her life caused the eating disorder to rear its ugly head. After two treatment centers in a three-year

period, we're very aware that relapse is not uncommon. We will continue to encourage continued outpatient therapy, praying that she's gaining strength and tools to deal with whatever the future holds."

– A Fighter

Below are six thoughts to help you move forward in your decision-making. You will have to weigh your options with honest conversation evaluating the stage of life your child, your family, and you are currently in. You are not alone in this fight. Please know that good positive treatment can be beautifully life-altering. Be creative, be persistent, and above all, be honest with yourself and your loved ones.

Ask for Help

Ask for help and referrals from anyone you know who has walked (or currently is walking) this path before you. We say this over and over in this book because you are not alone, and you do not have to start from scratch. There already is a square one (and much, much more!). Reach out for help.

Collaborate with Professionals

How do you choose which "treatment" is right for your child and/ or loved one? Set up a consultation with a licensed eating-disorder specialist and meet with them face to face. If you are not in the same city, try FaceTiming and/or Skyping. Explain the situation, and as they offer opinions ask yourself, *Does this feel right? Is there hope in the message? Is this professional understanding our needs? Are we communicating fluidly?* When choosing which treatment option seems best for your child, family and you, collaborating with the potential professionals is critical. When you make a final choice (and if your decision does not work as planned, change it), be prepared to work together, pool resources, participate in offering your understanding of the current circumstances, and communicate openly. Then, be prepared to listen and learn.

Do Your Own Research

We recommend you do some research on your own to find the most affordable and suitable treatment for your family. All family dynamics are different, so you must be realistic with what works for your child, you, and your family. For instance, the center's location, the appropriateness for your child's age, or whether it has a religious affiliation or not are all important details to consider.

Stay Within Your Financial Means

You must try to be realistic and know there are limits to when, how, and how much one can spend on treatment. We will do almost anything in the world to help heal our child, but we try to be as reasonable as possible. You, as the adult, are responsible for making the monetary decisions; your child is not. Do not discuss cost and all problems associated with this expensive venture, especially if there is financial strain. It will trigger shame and put undue burdens upon your child. Do what you can financially to help your child, but recognize and respect your monetary limits.

If you have a self-sufficient adult child living outside of the home and carrying his or her own insurance plan, then you can, and should, talk financial details. If they are invested financially, they will be more serious about the treatment.

Mind Your Physical and Mental Health

There will be times when you are maxed out. Be considerate of your own physical limits and react accordingly. Take care of your physical health, however that works best for you. There will be times when you are emotionally spent. Again, stop and access your needs for clarity of mind. Please know that there are times when you have to say, "I can't," either physically, emotionally and/or financially. Do not torment yourself over feeling inadequate or unable to spend a particular amount of money for treatment. You may be doing your absolute best, but you are human. We do have limitations.

Seek Your Own Worth

Often much emphasis and devotion is spent on teaching patients to "love your body." This is a common theme in treatment. It is great if you love your body—few really do—but what if we accept, appreciate, and feel gratitude for our body, but love our soul?

> *"After my daughter has been taught this healing concept of love your body, she's finally asking, 'Why do we have to love our bodies? Why can't we put the emphasis and attention on other things that have nothing to do with our looks or our bodies—like our talents, our hearts, our interests, our future? Taking our minds OFF of our bodies is the most beneficial thing to help with our recovery!'"*
> – A Listening Mother

A *New York Times* article dated March 2016 notes that a decade ago there were twenty-two treatment centers for eating disorders.

Today there are over seventy-five in America alone.[29]

Is this because eating disorders are rampant in our Western society? Yes, that's one reason. In 2008 the Mental Health Parity and Addition Equity Act [30]was passed, which required insurance companies to cover mental illness such as eating disorders and addiction treatment. Then in 2010 Obama's Affordable Care Act[31] furthered the cause.

> *Please refer to the appendix in this book for more details on MHPAEA on the Affordable Care Act.*

This burst in growth gives parents/caregivers options as treatment centers have different philosophies towards restoring the health of their patients. It also makes choosing treatment more complex. Location, financial wherewithal, in-network facilities, the patient's health condition, and age all play a role in your decision. It is a personal decision depending on your desire for faith-based treatment versus secular, inner-city locations versus rural acres in the countryside and/or a hospital setting and philosophy, versus a comfortable center that offers fun activities. We cannot recommend the best and/or comment on what we perceive to be the worst treatment centers, but we can assure you that the earlier you get help for your loved one, the higher the probability for full and comprehensive healing. We can also tell you that relying on professionals to help your child reduces the burden for a caregiver.

If you think it is time (or past time) to send your child to treatment, please know that hundreds of us have endured the dilem-

29. Goode, Erica. "Centers to Treat Eating Disorders Are Growing, and Raising Concerns." The New York Times. The New York Times, 14 Mar. 2016. Web. 08 Nov. 2016. www.nytimes.com/2016/03/15/health/eating-disorders-anorexia-bulimia-treatment-centers.
30. "Mental Health and Substance Use Disorder Parity." Mental Health and Substance Use Disorder Parity. N.p., n.d. Web. 08 Nov. 2016. www.dol.gov/ebsa/mentalhealthparity.
31. Muñoz, Cecilia. "The Affordable Care Act and Expanding Mental Health Coverage." The White House. The White House, 21 Aug. 2013. Web. 08 Nov. 2016. www.whitehouse.gov/blog/2013/08/21/affordable-care-act-and-expanding-mental-health-coverage.

ma, and you will get through to the other side. You will.

Doing the hard time is momentarily painful, but the payoff for your loved one's future is worth it.

Does This Feel Familiar?

My Best College Friend

"She had been back from inpatient treatment for about three weeks the first time we ventured out to dinner together. The act was familiar enough for both of us, picking our path across the campus lawn in the fading light to navigate around a group of kids playing touch football. The air was still so warm that even she couldn't be cold, and as we walked, we talked about the unremarkable items of the day in a remarkably ordinary way. Surely it was just a handful of months, but it seemed so incredibly long ago that we were last this at ease in each other's company.

In truth, her downward spiral had been a very quick one, and probably not entirely unpredictable. We met as fresh-faced freshmen girls, both the furthest from home we had ever been for any significant period of time, both so excited to finally be there. Our connection was pretty much immediate and, in the way of dorm life, we became inseparable in what, in retrospect, seemed like a matter of minutes. There were several months of relative normalcy; just long enough to forget there was ever a time when we weren't friends. Long enough to be convinced we knew each other better than anyone else knew us. And then, before I even noticed what was happening, this sweet friend of mine became a different person altogether. This girl, widely known for her belly laughs, for her buoyancy, her light. . . . even with our special brand of best-friend humor, I couldn't coax a smile from her.

Ever the fixer, I tried my damnedest to break through the wall that seemed to have gone up around her. I had dealt with eating disorders before; I knew how this worked. I figured persistence was key. I tried to make her talk any chance I got. Worse, I tried to make her eat. I barked orders, I pushed, I chided, I threatened. She withdrew further. I redoubled my efforts. I labeled her behaviors. I studied the smallest details of her life, trying to micromanage any stressors but somehow only adding to her pain. And eventually, inevitably, everything good about our friendship evaporated, leaving nothing but bitterness behind.

And so it felt like an unexpected gift that evening, as we walked to dinner, as we ordered our matching salads and embraced our return to normalcy, when I felt a streak of hope reach up through my chest. I was going to get her back, and it was going to be exactly what it had been before. That perfect, sunny relationship we had, where we just "got" each other and all we ever did was giggle. I think she must have felt bold that evening too, encouraged perhaps by a similar hope, because when I suggested we cap off the night with an old tradition—a soft-serve cone from McDonald's. She agreed.

I knew she was trying. I knew she wanted to eat that ice cream. I even knew that she knew how much it meant to me that she eat it. But she couldn't stomach it, and suddenly I was livid. Eat the freaking ice cream already! After two bites, she was sick.

We walked back to the dorm in a shattered silence, disgusted and disappointed in ourselves and in each other, and we didn't speak again for several months. I couldn't look at her without feeling this terrible simultaneous mix of frustration and anger, overlaid with embarrassment at my own lack of empathy or understanding. I knew about eating disorders. I knew how this worked. So why was I so mad at her?

I learned a lot about myself in trying to process those feelings. I learned that I am not a particularly patient person. Further, my patience is at its most limited when dealing with those closest to me. I learned that I am controlling, and I detest situations I cannot manage. I realized I am not the great listener I envisioned myself to be. I've been working on all of that. I also learned I cannot fix someone else. I've learned that I have a tendency to be very unforgiving when it comes to my own bad behavior, a trait that has yet to prove itself helpful. I learned that no amount of reading or talking or researching could ever really make me understand what it is like to have an eating disorder. That there's a big difference between saying "it's about control" and actually having any clue what that might mean. I realized how easily disappointment and fear turn into something else entirely, and as a result, I'm much more likely to step back and inspect my feelings nowadays, just to be sure I'm dealing with what I think I'm dealing with. I have also learned that time is an impossible concept when you've been hurt, and that healing consists of many of shades of gray.

Years later, I can say we salvaged the relationship. I can say we are friends who made it through a really terrible thing. But we are not the same friends we were, and I know now that hoping for that was hoping for too much. We are friends who have spent a great many hours and an immeasurable quantity of tears trying to sort out just how we got so hurt by each other, and how we let go of that, how we make an eating disorder that never totally went away stop steering our friendship, and how we accept this changed and flawed version of our relationship as enough. But we are friends, and for that, I am grateful."

– A Friend

11
MEDICAL HEALTH INSURANCE FOR EATING DISORDERS

[Currently confusing and seemingly
ever-changing scenarios!]

Yes, we have to deal with this too. Educating ourselves on eating-disorder insurance can be monotonous, so try to be patient. This is a good time to recruit a knowledgeable friend, family member, associate, or acquaintance for help. We have all had to deal with insurance companies—some with good experiences, and others with very, very, very frustrating experiences. In the end, you alone and/or with your spouse/partner will have to make personal decisions regarding money. By no means do we claim to know everything about the fast-changing mental health policies and coverage, but we will share with you what we do know. Note: Hospital emergency rooms, in-patient care, treatment centers, and some professionals will guide you through the insurance protocol. We believe good care is paramount, so to the best of your ability, find the best-suited treatment facilities/doctors possible and begin working on how to financially afford the cost.

Advocates continue to fight for more sufficient coverage. Sadly, it is frustrating to discover that insurance often covers only a small portion of the expenses for psychiatric conditions (like eating disorders) and the treatment thereof, but that is changing. Though many insurance policies come with restrictions regarding mental-health coverage, they are required by law to treat mental illness equal to medical illnesses. Finding doctors and treatment in-network is less expensive.

If the doctors and treatment you prefer are out-of-network, you can personally submit expenses and file out-of-network with your insurance carrier. Out-of-network help is covered at a lower percent and/or not at all. Learning how to work within the system and obtaining adequate coverage is possible. Below are some suggestions, and please refer to appendix for some recommended websites.

What Could a Mom Do Now?

Review Your Insurance Policy

Is your insurance policy an Indemnity Policy (few are), a Preferred Provider Organization PPO, or a Health Maintenance Organization HMO? Eating disorders are covered under the "Mental Health" section of your insurance policy. Review your policy and understand what percent of mental-health coverage you have and how it works. For example, are there deductibles in your policy? Is there a defined number of "visits" allowed per year? Is there an annual cap expenses for mental health?

There is a number on the back of your insurance card. Call the number and ask about your coverage of benefits. Ask any and all questions you want to understand. Write down the answers for future reference.

The Mental Health Parity Equity Act of 2008 mandated the same coverage for mental illness as medical illness but was only for employers with at least fifty employees offering health plans with benefits. Then the Affordable Care Act was passed, and now mental-health coverage is mandated for individuals, and the individual can-

> *For more information please refer to the appendix in the back of the book.*

not be discriminated against if they have a pre-existing condition.[32]

Recognize What Your Insurance Company Needs from You

Your insurance provider does not know you individually, and big carriers have thousands of patients. Insurance companies are required to confirm and seek answers regarding your request, so to determine coverage, they must confirm legitimacy of the illness and pay for "reasonable" treatment. There is not standardization from carrier to carrier; policies vary depending on the negotiation. Large companies are able to negotiate insurance to best fit the needs of their employees while private insurance is not as flexible. To better help them assess a situation we recommend you:

- Gather letters from professionals validating the diagnosis and need for treatment.
- To the best of your ability, supply your insurance company with proof and evidence of the patient's diagnosis and treatment needs.
- Keep a copy of everything.
- Take and keep fastidious notes.
- In your persistence, be as professional and level-headed as possible. All calls are recorded, so keep your cool. Eat-

---

32. Gram, Judith. "New Insurance Policies Must Cover Mental Illness." Chicago Tribune Company, LLC, 9 Jan. 2014. Web. www.anad.org/category/news.

ing-disorder treatment is not as easy to evaluate as the medical needs for broken bones.

Contact Your Insurance Company (the Earlier the Better)

Contact your insurance provider before your child starts formal treatment. (Unless your child is in medical danger—in that case, go to the nearest emergency room for help.) You will most likely be assigned a "case manager," sometimes referred to as a nurse case manager. If you're not assigned to a case manager, ask for one. Ask to speak with someone who has experience with eating disorders. Get to know your case manager by name. If you truly do not connect with his or her personality, ask for a different case manager. Ask as many questions as you find necessary to understand your policy. We suggest you:

- Get comfortable up front, knowing you will have to be persistent. Continue to call, and do not hesitate to ask for a supervisor.
- Ask for help and advice from your insurance agent.
- Ask for a copy of your policy. Have the insurance company email, fax, or mail the policy for your review. Make sure, up front, that you understand the coverage for mental health. Get a hard copy (printed version) of the benefits from your insurance company and/or a digital copy.
- Get a signed waiver if your child is eighteen or older. This allows you to work with the insurer on your child's behalf.
- Engage your spouse's help if you are married and covered under the same policy. Often, one spouse is the primary insured, so help each other navigate.
- Communicate and ask questions of the professionals your child, your family, and you have committed to work-

ing with. Most professionals and treatment centers are very helpful.

Educate and Update Yourself and Your Insurance Provider

When having a discussion with your insurance agent, insurance company, doctor's office, human-resources department at work, etc., be appreciative for the help and easy to work with in hopes of making the process as smooth as possible. By no means are we suggesting you be a pushover, and please do not give up trying to get what you want or need. Be an advocate (and a stern advocate), but to the best of your ability, do not be difficult or rude. Entitled, offensive behavior causes more problems. Share regulations, guidelines, and new laws currently instated and/or currently being reviewed.

Below are examples of new and existing laws.[33]

For details please refer to the appendix in the back of this book.

- Patient Protection Affordable Care Act (PPACA)
- Thursday, January 9, 2014 Mental Illness Covered in New Insurance Policies
- Mental Health Parity and Addiction Equity Act of 2008 (MHPAEA)
- 2010 Obama's Affordable Care Act

---

33. *The Mental Health Parity and Addiction Equity Act (MHPAEA)*. N.p., n.d. Web. 08 Nov. 2016. www.cms.gov/CCIIO/Programs-and-Initiatives/Other-Insurance-Protections.

"The emotional toll that is felt when caring for an unhealthy child is exhausting and adding the financial burden onto what all are going through is an added stress that none of us wish we had to experience. But, illness in any form costs money. For those of us who are insured, we are fairly knowledgeable and accustomed to pulling out our insurance card at the doctor's office when our child is sick. And, if our child has an injury and needs an X-ray then that is an understood process that we know. But, when one is faced with the reality that their child has a mental disorder and the need is for psychological services . . . then we are thrown into the world of one that we hoped to never hear: "We don't accept insurance," "you pay in full," "you're out of network," "good luck getting your insurance company to reimburse you," etc. Ongoing therapy is expensive. I always like to lighten things up by saying that we will continue to grow more "money trees" in our backyard. Although that is a fabricated pipe-dream, we do often exceed our monetary capacity in desperation to help! All of us will do anything we can to help a child that hurts and that includes paying for treatment. I would like to share that all is not lost when it comes to medical insurance. I recommend that you call your insurance company and specifically ask what your policy might cover. Secondly, always get a receipt/statement from every doctor you see whether it's a therapist, psychologist, psychiatrist, etc. and always remind then to put their code numbers on the receipt. We send every charge into our insurance company. Sometimes we actually will get a partial reimbursement. It never hurts to try and collect . . . after all, you are paying

for insurance whether it's used or not. It's a shame that many disorders that fall into the psychological category are usually not covered; whereas if your child breaks their leg then all is easily processed. There are current efforts to improve this and my hope is that the day will come when mental and psychological disorders are proportionally equal in coverage as any illness. Until then, I encourage you to submit and stay with it."

— A Determined Mom, Navigating the
Complex Insurance System

Get a Confirmed Diagnosis

Most insurance companies require a confirmed diagnosis by an eating-disorder specialist. Get a diagnosis so that the eating disorder and associated mental and physical health issues are properly documented. Ask the doctor for the diagnostic paperwork/digital assessment that you can forward to your insurance company. In some cases, the doctor will fill with your insurance company.

Get Pre-authorization

Inform your insurance provider about doctors/treatment you are planning to see and try to get "pre-qualified." Some doctors will not be in your network. You'll have to make a personal financial decision regarding this issue. Remember to ask for a list of in-network professionals in your area. Potentially, this step could take a while. If your child is in medical danger, seek help immediately or go to the nearest emergency room.

Confirm "Billing Codes" Used by Doctors and Professionals

Billing codes are something we have found to be very important in regards to validating payout from an insurance company. Confer with your professionals to insure the diagnosis is filled under the correct billing code. These codes are to medically describe the disease, the symptoms, and the condition. It is not important to fully understand the coding system, but it is important that your doctor assigns the code that corresponds to the eating disorder and all co-existing illnesses. Ask your doctor about the billing codes they have assigned to your case.

According to the National Eating Disorders Association, there are certain rules and government regulations about who can perform services and how those services must be "coded."[34]

> *For more information please refer to the appendix in the back of the book.*

If You Are Employed

If you are insured through work, go visit with your human-resources department and obtain a copy of benefits for your review. Get an education from them about the coverage possible and how to go about obtaining the best possible treatment for your loved one. Remember, since the employer pays for the insurance, it is

---

34. "…when a service is provided by a doctor or facility, a billing code is needed to obtain reimbursement for services. Certain rules and government regulations how services must be coded and who can perform these services. Different types of facilities and different healthcare professionals must use codes that apply to that type of facility and health professional. Also, if codes don't exist for certain services delivered in a particular setting, then facilities and health professionals have no way to bill for their services. Codes used for billing purposes are set up by various entities such as the American Medical Association, U.S. Medicare program, and the World Health Organization's International Classification of Diseases (National Eating Disorders Association)"

actually the employer who has control over what benefits are provided by the PPO/HMO.

Understand the Laws in Your State

Laws and regulations regarding coverage for eating disorders vary from state to state. Learn the laws in your home state of residence and communicate with your insurance provider to review new and existing state laws regarding coverage. Interestingly enough, some states have better insurance coverage for eating disorders than others, so be sure to do your research. Please refer to the next chapter (12) in regards to affording treatment and ideas on how to obtain insurance and affordable help.

Overwhelmed? So were we! Dealing with the insurance company and trying to get coverage for the illness while dealing with the emotions of an eating disorder seems impossible. It does take time and patience. Please ask for help. If you know your insurance provider or they live in the same city, consider meeting with them face to face.

In the article, "How Obama Care Improved Mental Health Coverage," the author Louise Norris notes how the Parity Laws and Affordable Care Act (ACA) are intentional in helping citizens obtain more adequate health insurance for "behavioral health coverage." As we write this book times are already changing. The future of health insurance is unpredictable.[35]

Our hope for you is that your doctors and/or treatment center of choice will be insurance advocates for you and your family. Many have personnel well-trained in coverage for all mental illnesses; we hope that person becomes a part of your village!

---

35. Norris, Louise. "How Obamacare Improved Mental Health Coverage." *Healthinsuranceorg Obamacare and Its Future under a New President Comments.* N.p., 16 Feb. 2016. Web. 14 Nov. 2016. www.healthinsurance.org/blog/2016/02/16/how-obamacare-improved-mental-health-coverage.

There is new legislation being reviewed, conversations being had, and activists trying to get more adequate coverage for mental health. Insurance is personal with both fluctuating and immovable policies, so you must deal directly with your carrier. There are note pages at the end of the section to take notes and record medical health insurance questions and answers.

Does This Feel Familiar?

Differentiates Between the Lies She Was Hearing and the Truth

"I am the mother of four daughters married to a wonderful man who is very involved in raising our children and shepherding them into adulthood. My husband and I were deliberate and focused on never having any of our girls battle an eating disorder. I had heard what that looked like and we were not going there. As my girls neared their preteen and teen years I read as much material and attended as many lectures on eating disorders as possible. I thought I totally had a handle on this one. Our home was a safe place where we didn't focus on our bodies or food. We played "Catch the Lie" when we watched movies, TV or read magazines—pointing out the lies the culture puts out. Then, one day, a friend who had walked that road with her daughter mentioned that I might want to carefully watch one of our daughters. She was growing painfully thin right before our eyes and we hadn't noticed. As she was entering her sophomore year in high school, we started paying very close attention. True, she was not eating much but we assumed it was part of her body changing as she matured. Her spirits seemed happy and content. It wasn't until we read a poem she had written that it hit us.

She wrote that she felt like she was trapped in chains and couldn't break out. There was no mention of food, just the feeling of being in bondage to something unspoken. When I asked her about the poem she broke down and admitted that she indeed was in a battle that was bigger than her. She couldn't find her way out. She was terrified. So were we.

I am so thankful my husband was determined to understand the pain our daughter was feeling and to walk every step of this road with us. Some fathers cannot handle it. With his support and her honesty and desire for victory over this, we sought a counselor who understood eating disorders. We didn't want to overreact but we sure didn't want to ignore this either.

How did this happen? What caused this? Where did we go wrong? Like any parent we just knew if we understood the cause we could fix the problem. As our daughter continued to be honest with us about her emotions and her constant battle we saw that we needed more help than just weekly counseling. As a side note, I must mention that there are so many treatment options it is overwhelming. It is critical that you do your research to find the best fit for your child and your family. Determining what type treatment is affordable, who offers services in-network with your insurance carrier and what treatment is needed takes tenacity. If you find it's not a good fit once you are in don't be afraid to move on. We made the sober decision to enter our child into an outpatient program at our local children's hospital.

It was there that she began the process of getting healthy physically so she could get healthy mentally. It was also there that our entire family entered into deep introspection on who we were individually and as a family unit. The saying goes "you are only as healthy as your least healthy family member." We were all hurting as we fought to understand her pain and struggles. This was especially difficult for her sisters.

We began a combination of family therapy and therapy for my husband and I alone. I think both were critical in helping us better understand our family dynamics and how they may have played a role in her pain and confusion. It was vital for the three sisters to get involved so they could learn how to support and love their sister along the way, as well as work through their own pain. Two sisters are older and they could totally engage. The youngest daughter was still too young to fully comprehend what was going on but we included her as much as appropriate. Thus continued the delicate balance of guiding each of our girls in an age appropriate fashion. As for my husband and me, counseling on *disordered eating was critical. I will say, in the beginning, we felt like all of the "professionals" were overly aggressive in trying to determine where the fault lay. It felt like they assumed it was a parenting issue, or perhaps a mothering issue. Through the process, though, we were all able to slowly understand each other better. It was humbling and worth our daughter's hope for healing to be honest and vulnerable. We attended counseling while she was in outpatient care and then she continued weekly counseling once she was discharged. She continued meeting with the therapist regularly throughout the remainder of her high school career and periodically through college. She also saw a certified nutritionist on a weekly basis. We didn't realize at the time that most ED patients can be dishonest and deceptive. We quickly learned to appreciate the fact that she was being sincere and honest with us and that she didn't want to be in that situation any more than we wanted her to be in it. This mindset greatly enhanced her recovery.*

Were we scared? Absolutely. Perhaps we always will be a little. We walked on pins and needles around her for years and I think to this day we all still treat her a little more gingerly out of fear of a relapse.

Was it my fault? You always hear about Mother's Guilt—it is a very real thing. I'm sure childhood issues that I brought into my adult reality didn't help. Having grown up in a large family with a small mother and an obese father, my biggest fear was that I would end up like my dad. There was often family conflict which included a dose of sarcasm and hurtful condescension. I have purposed to raise my own children with more grace.

My husband and I are so thankful for our house full of girls, but it is a balancing act of rollercoaster emotions on a constant basis. We have always fought for our girls and our family as a whole. We always will. One of our mottos is "Sisters are closer than friends." Some days it didn't feel true but we persevered in teaching them to love and forgive. Families are fragile and need extra love and grace.

My job as Mom was to be her safe place. The more consumed she was with the ED the more she pulled away from her friends. It seemed to us that the ED was her best friend, but that was a relationship based on lies. The key was for her to learn how to differentiate between the lies she was hearing and the Truth she knew in her soul—that she was good and worthy and perfectly knit together. God didn't make a mistake when He made her just the way she was.

We had a team of professionals that advised us through the battle and my role in her recovery became clear. Love her, support her, hold her accountable with a touch of grace and encourage her to keep moving forward. When she was overwhelmed and in tears, struggling to fight, I learned not to push her with comments like "Just change! Just stop restricting!" Hug her and tell her it's ok to feel what she was feeling. I encouraged her to lean into her feelings, talk about them and write them down. We approached the ED as a lie she was hearing. She had to learn how to identify the lie she was believing, and then how to replace the lies with the voice of truth—even if she didn't believe it yet.

On a practical level, planning meals was overwhelming. I helped her plan her meals and made sure I provided all the resources she needed to succeed such as a variety of healthy food options and mini food scales (which her nutritionist suggested). We would go through her food plan and talk about it. During meals do not talk about food or put pressure on her to eat her dinner. Mom needs to be the "safe" place. I made it a practice to tell her daily that I believed in her. She told me much later that knowing we believed in her gave her the necessary strength to fight and win. I was in awe of her courage in fighting the battle.

I want to mention the importance of finding a trusted set of friends whom you can lean on and who will support your family. We were fortunate enough to have that. This allowed us to be totally honest and not feel the need to keep secrets. Not only were they there to love my husband and me, but some of their children were also purposeful in loving and supporting our three other daughters as well as encouraging our child who was sick.

Don't lose hope. Don't give up. Believe in your child and their ability to fight. There can be victory.

Ten years down the road, our daughter is thriving. She is healthy, peaceful and happily married to a wonderfully supportive young man. She is our hero."

– The Mother of a Fifteen-Year-Old
High School Sophomore Daughter

12

UNABLE TO AFFORD TREATMENT AND/OR NOT INSURED?

[Help is available but not always necessarily easy.]

Worried because you are not insured? You are not alone, and there are ways to get help. Treatment is expensive, and we all have worried about the cost. To find free (or low-cost) help, you will need to be diligent as you advocate for your child and family.

According to The Elisa Project (TEP), who is dedicated to the development of healthy children and adolescents by promoting the awareness and prevention through education, support, and advocacy, treatment does exist for those who have no money or insurance benefits. It is often difficult to locate, though. The Elisa Project recommends options such as counseling centers at work, school or community facilities, and/or psychiatry departments in medical schools. TEP also has a helpline. When someone calls, he or she will receive a return call and a live person to talk to.[36]

For more information on The Elisa Project, please see the appendix in the back of the book.

---

36. www.theelisaproject.org.

> *"Accessing ED resources for recovery with little or no financial resources is tough, but not impossible. It takes diligence, persistence, creativity and a loud voice. Remember, you are fighting against a disease that is smart, cunning and does not want you well. In seeking treatment you'll hit many walls, but you must not give up efforts or hope. That's what ED wants you to do. Help is out there, but it's like mining for diamonds or panning for gold."*
> — Kimberly Martinez,
> Executive Director at The Elisa Project

What Could a Mom Do Now?

You will have to educate yourself and dig deeper in your research, always asking for help. Whatever treatment center or doctor you speak with, ask them up front and directly if they will consider taking your case for free; many do pro-bono work. It does not mean they will say yes, but it does not hurt to ask.

Below are suggestions on how to potentially receive financial aid for the treatment of eating disorders. You can find more information about many of the organizations and policies in the appendix in the back of the book.

Low-cost Health Coverage

If your child requires treatment, and you have no medical insurance, refer to the Foundation for Health Coverage Education as they can help determine whether you or someone you know is eligible for free or low-cost health coverage.[37]

You should also consider studying Health Network, Obamacare short-term health insurance. [38]

Cannot Afford to Pay for Help

If you cannot afford professional services for your child and/or family, call The National Eating Disorders Association Helpline. The number is in the appendix at the back of this book. Ask questions, and they will guide you through their website if necessary.

Seek Out Free Services and Care in Your Community

Ask for advice and/or referrals from individuals in gratis positions. For example; consider meeting with:

- Moms and caretakers who are dealing with the same issue
- School counselors
- School nurses
- Youth ministers
- Local YMCA leaders
- Local "teaching hospitals"
- Community mental health agencies in your city
- Leaders in medical schools and universities in your city (Often there are free clinics operated by residents in training and supervised by faculty.)

---

37. Laboratory, Orbital. "Foundation for Health Coverage Education." Foundation for Health Coverage Education. N.p., n.d. Web. 08 Nov. 2016. www.coverageforall.org.
38. "Health Network Group, LLC Obamacare." Obamacarenet. N.p., n.d. Web. 08 Nov. 2016. www.obamacare.net.

*Consider also searching the internet for free clinical trials in your area.

Negotiate with the Doctors and/or Treatment Centers Regarding Cost

Explain your situation and ask for assistance. Inquire about scholarship programs. Some treatment centers are supplementary—funded by county, state, or federal funds—and potentially required to make care available. You will never know unless you ask.

Mentor Programs and Scholarships

There are programs and scholarships all over the country. You will need to do some of your own research as there are more than what you see below, and the list available is updated frequently. Listed here are scholarships we are familiar with. Please refer to the appendix in the back of the book for contact information and website addresses.

- Mentor Connect
- Manna Fund
- Moon Shadow's Spirit
- Project Heal
- The Gail R. Schoenback Foundation
- Clinical Trials
- Lisa's Light of Hope
- Mercy's Ministries
- Kirsten Haglund Foundation
- Eating Disorders Anonymous

Online Parent Forum

This is a good one! Parents Supporting Parents "Around the

Dinner Table" is an online forum of parents from all around the world. It is run by Families Empowered and Supporting Treatment of Eating Disorders (F.E.A.S.T.).[39]

> *For more contact information, please refer to appendix inthe back of the book.*

Workbook

Whether you are able to actively partake in therapy or not, we recommend the workbook, *When your Child has an Eating Disorder: A Step-by-Step Workbook for Parents and Caregivers*. It is a good place to start and/or restart.[40]

Online Funding Platforms: Crowdfunding

Medical expenses can be outrageously expensive, and many people are turning to the internet for help. Use technology to your advantage. Raise treatment funds by crowdsourcing, a popular way of getting financial support from large groups of people around the world who donate through an online platform. People donate because they want to give. There is not payback. There are many "crowdfunding" sites to explore, so please do so. Below are a few ideas of medically-minded sites. Please see the appendix for contact information.

- Give Forward
- GoFundMe
- You Caring

---

39. "Around the Dinner Table." *Families Empowered and Supporting Treatment of Eating Disorders*. N.p., n.d. Web. feast-ed.org.
40. Natenshon, Abigail. *When Your Child Has an Eating Disorder: A Step-by-step Workbook for Parents and Other Caregivers*. San Francisco: Jossey-Bass, 1999. Print.

- FundRazr
- Kickstarter
- DonateTo
- JustGive

Online eTherapy and Therapy Apps

With the existence of the internet, most anything can be found—even online therapy for eating disorders. eHealth delivers health care, and eTherapy provides online treatment for depression, anxiety, and now eating disorders. One of the therapies is called CBTe (cognitive behavioral therapy online). It is free, personalized, and intriguing! We cannot recommend eTherapy only because none of us have tried it. We do recommend you research further and see if eTherapy, specifically for eating disorders, fits in your lifestyle and pocketbook.

On Healthline.com there are ten apps listed to be the Best Eating Disorder Apps of 2016. [41]On Buzzfeed.com seventeen apps are reviewed for people recovering from an eating disorder. [42]These apps are either free or at the most $6.00. Some work on iPhones, others only on Android, and a few cross over to different smart phones. Face-to-face therapy is, by far, the best-case scenario. But, if you want to investigate these apps because you feel you cannot afford a therapist, then you should. Please use discernment, ask questions, do a test run, and if they help, why not engage?

You will have to be creative in obtaining financial help for treatment. Are you comfortable asking family members for money? Do you know an "angel donor" who would give you the money? Are you comfortable asking friends for financial support? If

41. Schaefer, Anna. "The Best Eating Disorder Apps of 2016." Healthline. N.p., 24 May 2016. Web. 08 Nov. 2016. www.healthline.com/health/eating-disorders.
42. Buzzfeed. "17 Therapy Apps." BuzzFeed Media. N.p., n.d. Web. 08 Nov. 2016.

you know you cannot pay them back, be honest. The donation is a gift, and you have to get comfortable with that.

Remember, your asking for help is for your child's health and life. Can you separate yourself and ask on their behalf? A good rule of thumb in fundraising is to say to yourself, *If capable, would I give money to that person if they asked?* If the answer is yes, most likely they will give to you. Remember, self-worth is based in one's own perspective. What if we turn it around and think of it as allowing others the gift of giving? You are giving that person the ability to give. Giving fulfills purpose and is a wonderful feeling, but you have to be willing to receive.

None of us recommends taking out a loan or a lien again your home mortgage. You might consider talking with a banker, but please do not put yourself and your family in an irreconcilable financial situation. Some of us have had to, and it took years to recover.

Please consider asking your friends and family for help first.

Does This Feel Familiar?

Thank You

My Dear Friend,

How can I thank you enough for the abundance of love and support you have given us these past few weeks? You have a gift of loving others and the innate qualities of a natural caregiver. And . . . you do so unselfishly. With great passion you feel and sense others fears and frustrations. I appreciate your sincere love and concern. (I owe you some hand cream!)

There is no doubt it takes a village and how blessed we are to be in your village. You have truly loved your neighbor as yourself and we are so grateful for that love. Thank you for being such a wonderful friend . . . not to mention cook, errand runner, housekeeper, drink provider, surrogate mother, shoulder to lean on and confidant.

A preacher once said from the pulpit, 'When we choose to love we also take the chance of pain.' In a sense, I know at different levels you too have felt the times of excruciatingly painful moments over these past few weeks. It's a bond all mothers share and a risk all of us are willing to take as a parent. We chose to love. And wow, it can hurt to the core. No doubt I will second-guess myself and wonder how we got where we are but . . . we are here and by the grace of God and with His guidance, I have to believe the future is full of promise. Not easy. It's time now to look forward and not back . . . to aid in her healing as we patiently live life one day at a time.

If anyone is capable of working through this issue, it's our daughter. That strong will and discipline will serve her well. No one ever said it would be easy but the burdens are certainly lightened by the support of friends like you. I just don't know how people make it without family and/or good friends and deep faith. Perhaps that is the home to fear and anger, when one feels like there is nowhere to turn.

Thank you for loving our child, thank you for your prayers of healing, your sense of humor, your amazing devotion and financial support. I guess it's really true, What goes around comes around . . . thanks for being part of our come around!

Love always,
Your Neighbor

13 INNOVATIVE TREATMENTS AND THERAPIES

[Be creative, look beyond your boundaries, and be
open-minded to new ways of healing.]

There are new strategies being developed in eating-disorder recovery all the time. The ideas below do not cover everything, so
please do your own research, and always check with your licensed
professionals/doctors before proceeding with a new treatment.

By innovative, we mean treatments that are relatively new,
out of the box, novel, and sometimes unusual. Below are some
of those ideas and methodologies. Innovative techniques are designed to work as one part of the whole of a treatment team and
often in combination with conventional medicine.

Discussed below are fifteen options we have found useful:
naturopathic medicine, integrative medicine and doctors, integrative psychiatry, traditional Chinese medicine/acupuncture,
yoga, EMDR, extended care after-treatment, SFBT, logotherapy,
Emotional Intelligence, hypnosis, equine therapy, faith practices,
meditation, and spiritual healing. We refer to "natural" ways of
healing as innovative, but truthfully, many of them have been
around longer than conventional biomedicine. (For more detailed

information, please refer to the appendix in the back of the book.)

What Could a Mom Do Now?

Educate yourself on options for healing outside of the traditional medical protocol. The list below is a beginning with some referrals, but you will need to extend the research for help in the area where you live. There is not an order of preference or endorsement. If you are already practicing natural healing, we suggest you visit with your doctors/practitioner about their expertise in eating disorders. If they are not experienced in working with eating-disordered patients, ask for a referral. Be both open-minded and discerning as you discover new avenues of healing.

Naturopathic Medicine

Dr. Sheri Lewis, ND, explains naturopath medicine:

"A Naturopath, Licensed Doctor of Naturopathic Medicine can assess your child scientifically and deal naturally with imbalances in the brain potentially causing depression, anxiety, eating disorders and physical health issues. It is most effective to work simultaneously with medical doctors, therapists, and Naturopaths in the treatment of eating disorders. Licensed doctors of Naturopathic Medicine can assess your child scientifically (through blood work) and deal naturally with the imbalances in the brain and body through science. They are also licensed Nutritionists."

– Dr. Sheri Lewis, ND

Naturopaths (ND) base their practice on six timeless principles founded on medical tradition and scientific evidence[43]:

- Let nature heal.
- Identify and treat causes.
- Use low-risk procedures and healing compounds.
- Customize each diagnosis and treatment plan to fit each patient.
- Educate patients.
- Encourage self-responsibility and work closely with each patient.

> *For more information on naturopathic medicine,*
> *please refer to the appendix in the back of this book.*

Integrative Medicine and Doctor

Integrative medicine/therapies treat the mind, body, and spirit all at the same time, not just the physical frame of the human body. It emphasizes the healing of the entire person (bio-psycho-so-cio-spiritual dimensions) integrating the use of conventional and alternative health care. If you choose to go in this direction, make sure the professional is experienced in eating disorders. Many MDs combine integrative medicine and practices into their traditional work.

To find an integrative doctor close to you, start by researching the websites, **ABIHM Certified Holistic Certified Physicians**, **INIMH** (International Network of Integrative Mental Health[44]), and/or **ACAM** (The American Collage for Advancement in

---

43. "The Six Principles of Naturopathic Medicine." NCANP. N.p., n.d. Web. 09 Nov. 2016. www.ncanp.com/about-ncanp/naturopathic-medicine-principle.
44. "Integrative Mental Health." INIMH. N.p., n.d. Web. 09 Nov. 2016. www.nimh.org.

Medicine[45]).

Dr. James Greenblatt (MD) is a good person to learn from. In his book, *Answers to Anorexia*, Dr. Greenblatt speaks to mental illness and eating disorders. We believe his integrative medical approach works for the right patient. In Dr. Greenblatt's book and on his website, he discusses issues pertinent to eating-disorder recovery, integrative medical information, integrative psychiatry, and the importance of chemistry, balance, and brain clarity.[46]

Integrative Psychiatry

Rather than focusing just on an eating disorder per se, integrative psychiatry focuses on an individual's mental wellness while discovering who they are and how it affects them physically and emotionally. For example, integrative psychiatry promotes natural healing, combines alternative healing modalities, and addresses the origin of symptoms while focusing on mind, body, and environment.[47] To begin a search for doctors/practitioners in your state, try calling (800) 385-7863 or search the internet for additional information.

Traditional Chinese Medicine/Acupuncture

If "stepping out of the box" is a stretch for you and/or you need a declaration of validation, maybe this is a good place to look back into history. Learning that traditional Chinese medicine has been a medicinal part of the human race for thousands of years should give you some peace in using ancient healing practices

45. "American College for Advancement in Medicine (ACAM)." *American College for Advancement in Medicine* (ACAM). N.p., n.d. Web. 09 Nov. 2016. www.acam.org.

46. Greenblatt, James. *Answers to Anorexia: A Breakthrough Nutritional Treatment That Is Saving Lives*. North Branch, MN: Sunrise River, 2010. Www.jamesgreenblattmd.com. Web.

47. Miller, MD Elana. "The 10 Principles of Integrative Psychiatry." *The Huffington Post.* TheHuffingtonPost.com, n.d. Web. 09 Nov. 2016. www.huffingtonpost.com/elana-miller-md/integrative-psychiatry.

such as acupuncture, meditation, herbal remedies, and massage. Prevalent in eating-disorder cases is anxiety and depression; acupuncture has been used as a healing force for both. The energy flow throughout the body is called "chi." When the energy/chi is blocked, problems are exaggerated, the immune system is weakened, and illness sets in easier. Acupuncture stimulates certain places along the meridian pathway allowing the chi to flow naturally. This holistic treatment has proven healing in both anorexia and binge-eating issues.[48]

Yoga

Why yoga? Because it helps to ground an individual in body, soul, and mind. Yoga is a healthier alternative to compulsive exercise and can help reduce anger, depression, and/or frustration. Yoga calms compulsive behavior and egocentric thoughts about one's physical beauty. One idea for thought would be to engage in a yoga practice as a component of extended aftercare, thus a lifestyle.

There are many advocacy groups and hundreds of articles on the internet explaining why participating in a yoga practice is a healthy choice. For a person dealing with an eating disorder, we want to emphasis the following rational motives.

Yoga calms a busy (compulsive) mind. It is a stress release, helps keep you focused on the nearest present, and slows down an anxious system through controlled breath, increased blood flow, and enhanced serotonin. A yoga practice lowers cortisol, the chemical that can trigger two side effects from an eating disorder: depression and osteoporosis. And ultimately, a yoga practice affects your mental health as you learn to accept your physical self,

48. "Traditional Chinese Medicine: In Depth | NCCIH." U.S National Library of Medicine. U.S. National Library of Medicine, n.d. Web. 10 Nov. 2016. www.nccih.nih. gov/health/whatiscam/chineseme.

connect with a community, and thus feel more content and happy.

"As a therapist for teens and adult women struggling with the range of eating disorders, I recognized that as long as their minds and bodies remained disconnected, true healing and integration would be impossible. I am trained as a Clinical Psychologist, with post-doctoral training in eating disorder recovery. In my private practice, again and again, I observed clients who could intellectually understand the root causes of their symptoms as well as the methods of recovery. They knew what to do, but still could not get better. Knowing was not enough. Understanding on a cognitive level did not catalyze true change. In yoga, change happens from the inside out. It is a physical practice, sure, but that is only one of the eight limbs of yoga, known as asana. Yoga, which means to unite, or to yolk, connects the mind and body through the breath. When someone with an eating disorder, whose mind and body have been disconnected as a way of maintaining their symptoms, is asked to get inside of their body, to feel sensation, to experience proprioception, to get present, they are being offered an experience of healing. When someone whose thoughts are merged with their mind and whose capacity to tolerate frustration is offered the practice of meditation and of distancing thought from mind, they are given a tool that can greatly increase their capacity to be non-reactive and to tolerate frustration. Both the physical practice of yoga, and the mental tool of meditation can be powerful healing agents for those struggling to reconnect to their bodies after the severing of mind and body through an eating disorder.

And, "yoga" can cause great harm, if it is being taught and practiced as a way of exercise, burning calories, or body sculpting. For someone who may use these outcomes as fuel for their eating disorder, sending them to any yoga class, anywhere, is not wise.

When trying to find a way to offer the therapeutic tools of yoga to someone struggling with negative body image or an eating disorder, choose a teacher that has her/his own body confidence and that uses the teachings of yoga philosophy and practice as an agent of finding sensation, presence, and peace, not as a tool for weight loss or body shaming. Choose a teacher who cues for sensation and for presence, rather than celebrating poses or perfection."

– Melody Moore, Ph.D, RYT, founder of Embody Love Movement and Social Entrepreneur

Despite all of the positive side effects of a yoga practice we must be aware of "aggressive yoga practices" that are not appropriate for people struggling with an eating disorder. Hot yoga, power yoga, and any yoga used specifically for weight loss are not recommended. These types of practices are harmful to the patient both physically and psychologically.

EMDR, Eye Movement Desensitization and Reprocessing

Eye Movement Desensitization and Reprocessing (EMDR) is a type of counseling that can help change how you react to memories of traumatic experience. EMDR is

For more information and contact information on EMDR, please refer to the appendix in the back of the book.

used in trauma healing and often in helping individuals suffering from Post Traumatic Stress Syndrome. A trauma can trigger the onset of an eating disorder, and EMDR helps to deal with and then process the issue.

> *"EMDR (Eye Movement Desensitization and Reprocessing) is a psychotherapy that enables people to heal from the symptoms and emotional distress that are the result of disturbing life experiences. Repeated studies show that by using EMDR people can experience the benefits of psychotherapy that once took years to make a difference. It is widely assumed that severe emotional pain requires a long time to heal. EMDR therapy shows that the mind can in fact heal from psychological trauma much as the body recovers from physical trauma."*
>
> *— EMDR Institute, Inc.[49]*

Extended Care and Aftercare Treatment

Once someone is perceived as "healthy," it can be very scary for him or her to terminate therapy and/or leave the security of a treatment facility. No matter what treatment and/or therapy you and your child have been involved in, following up on their health is critical. Aftercare structure is imperative to prevent a relapse. Eating-disorder recovery should absolutely include follow-up care at home while one is reintegrating into their lives. Older patients may choose to live near or on the property of the treatment center depending upon that center's policies about aftercare. Some treat-

---

49. "EMDR Institute – Eye Movement Desensitization and Reprocessing Therapy." EMDR Institute. N.p., n.d. Web. 09 Nov. 2016. www.emdr.com.

ment centers follow their patients anywhere from one to five years post-treatment. This includes, but is not limited to, phone calls, mentorships, crisis management, and timely check-ups.

As life evolves, changes, and moves on, it is important to stay mindful of new and innovative coping skills for a life of full and proper healing. You and your family should always continue learning new coping skills.

> *"A well-conceived plan for aftercare is essential! Stepping from a cocoon of care and treatment back into the world ridden with angst and triggers is a relapse waiting to happen. Staying on the path of recovery is difficult with any disorder. Because food is necessary to live, the individual struggling with an eating disorder is being challenged every day. Having a therapist and dietician to help transition into a world surrounded by food choices is critical for success. Reinforcing positive self-loving mantras is also critical. Aftercare programs are set up to support the individual recovering and keep a watchful eye not just for accountability but so they don't feel alone."*
>
> – A Mom

At the very least, one year of aftercare with the patient's doctor/therapist is recommended for individuals once treatment is terminated. You and your team of doctors will need to determine the best avenue for successful extended aftercare.

Solution-focused Brief Therapy

SFBT is a therapy that focuses on solutions rather than problems. After thirty years of development, SFBT helps people improve their life and feel more confident and hopeful about the future they are able to achieve. SFBT focuses on solution-building based on the individual's positive traits and resources that can help build a future of hope. SFBT therapists do not spend a lot of time discussing past and/or present problems or causes. One idea to consider would be to engage in SFBT as a component of extended aftercare.[50]

Logotherapy

Viktor Frankl's logotherapy is based on the premise that a human being is motivated by a "will to meaning" and that we have freedom to find meaning and choose our attitude in any given circumstance. Logotherapy is the pursuit of meaning in one's life.[51]

One of our families helping to write this book is currently experiencing emotional relief and healing in their logotherapy sessions. They feel empowered and say this type of therapy has allowed them to release fears, be more vulnerable, feel joy just as they are, and find purpose.

> *"I wish we had found this type of therapy earlier. I felt like the therapist actually got me and could understand my desperate need for love and purpose. I was taught three different ways to discover meaning in my life; creating a work or doing a deed, encountering someone or experiencing something and lastly, I get to choose my attitude towards suffering and all circumstances. I was empowered to know that it is actually me that gets to make decisions regarding my life!"*
>
> – Logotherapy Fan

50. McFarland, Barbara. *Brief Therapy and Eating Disorders: A Practical Guide to Solution-focused Work with Clients.* San Francisco: Jossey-Bass, 1995. Print.
51. "Viktor Frankl Institute of Logotherapy." N.p., n.d. Web. 09 Nov. 2016. www.logotherapyinstitute.org.

The word logo originates from the Greek word logos, meaning the word of God, or principle of divine reason and creative order. That feels grounded and of the soul.[52]

Understanding Emotional Intelligence, EI/EQ

For decades, we have assessed intelligence with a score derived from standardized IQ tests. We believe assessing Emotional Intelligence is critical, if not more important, to the well-being of human beings. EI is often misunderstood, and we tend to view it as charisma or the "It" factor. EI is a non-verbal self-awareness and awareness of those around you. It is the ability to understand and manage our own emotions and also understand what others are experiencing emotionally. Understanding and developing mature Emotional Intelligence is consequential in the treatment of eating disorders. EI is actually intangible, yet it monitors our behavior, social skills, and self-awareness.

Many children, teens, young adults, and adults with eating disorders are both blessed and cursed with Emotional Intelligence. They feel deeper, hurt deeper, love deeper, are very sensitive, and have an overwhelming sense of heart power that gets confused in our social structure. Often a child cannot control their EI to guide behaviors and thinking; he or she tends to live in the highest degree of intense feelings. Ever wonder if the control of an eating disorder is affected by your child's EI? So, how does a mom help her child (no matter their age)? Here are a few thoughts:

- Listen, without judgment, in hopes that getting the emotions out will help them process through to a more rational side.
- Remind them to access coping skills and learn positive

---

52. www.en.oxforddictionaries.com/definition/logos

ways to solve problems. One easy coping skill is deep breathing, as it often helps one to calm down.

- Do not overreact in your responses.
- Role play.

Hypnosis

Adding hypnotherapy to the patient's treatment plan can be very beneficial. Hypnotherapy uses the power of suggestion to retrain thought and patterns among other things such as teaching relaxation techniques and confidence-building through guided imagery. There are lots of articles supporting the use of hypnotherapy when treating eating disorders. You will need to research a hypnotist familiar with eating disorders in your area.

Equine Therapy

Referred to as EAP (Equine Assisted Psychotherapy) and/or EFL (Equine Facilitated Learning), these treatments utilize the relationship between a horse and a patient—in our case, the patient is our loved one with an eating disorder. The human-horse relationship revolves around emotional healing and growth. There are many articles and websites about the mental and emotional benefits of equine therapy and people struggling with eating disorders.[53]

Referenced EEG

This technology has been used for over ten years in the treatment of eating disorders. Referenced EEG provides psychiatrists information to guide the choice of medications used for co-occurring emotional issues. There is no medication that cures eating disorders, but stabilizing co-existing illnesses is helpful in the healing

---

53. www.eatingdisorderhope.com.

process. The individual results of this technology show the psychiatrist what medications have been successfully used.[54]

Targeted Nutrition Therapy

Can vitamin and mineral deficiency be linked to developing anorexia? A lack of calcium, Vitamin B, and Omega-3 fatty acids are just three of the nutrients and minerals nutritional therapy targets. For example, zinc deficiency includes loss of appetite, weight loss, altered taste, depression, and absence of monthly periods. All five of these characteristics are prevalent in the development of anorexia. Zinc is also one of the most prevalent trace elements found in the human brain. Preteens and teenagers typically eat diets low in zinc. The traditional medical community has been slow to integrate zinc therapy, but if you see a naturopath she or he can run a blood test to check zinc levels.[55]

Online eTherapy and Therapy Apps

As discussed in chapter 12, online eTherapy and therapy apps for eating-disorder treatments is new and innovative. One of the therapies is called CBTe (cognitive behavioral therapy online).[56] It is free, personalized, and intriguing! We cannot recommend eTherapy only because none of us have tried it. We do recommend you research further and see if eTherapy, specifically for eating disorders, fits in your lifestyle and pocketbook.

---

54. Greenblatt, James, Dr. "Beyond The Basics – New Approaches To Treatment Of Anorexia Nervosa." Walden Eating Disorders Treatment. N.p., n.d. Web. 09 Nov. 2016.
55. "Targeted Nutrition Therapy." *Something Fishy*. N.p., n.d. Web. www.something-fishy.org/dangers/vitamins.
56. "ETherapy for Eating Disorders (CBTe)." *ETherapy for Eating Disorders (CBTe)*. N.p., n.d. Web. 09 Nov. 2016.

Faith Practices, Meditation, and Spiritual Healing

Last but not least (and actually, the most important), is the focus on faith practices, meditation, and spiritual healing in the treatment of eating disorders. We believe these non-secular practices are critical, so much so that faith practices deserve their own chapter. (Please refer to "Faith Practices.")

It is important to spend a little time detailing one of the most effective forms of a spiritual practice: meditation. Meditation has been found to increase happiness, lower stress and anxiety, aide in the treatment of depression, develop perspective, increase compassion, and lead to an overall higher sense of personal well-being. Nothing negative has ever come from meditation. The practice has been utilized as a healing tool for over 5,000 years, originating in the ancient Vedic traditions in what is now India. The practice has no religious affiliation and can be accessed by anyone regardless of his or her belief system or lack thereof. The task may sound daunting at first, but it is recommended to start with simply one minute of meditation per day and simply increase the time when one feels he or she is ready. Meditation is another method for gaining perspective and self-acceptance.

Meditation takes on many forms. Yoga, mantras repetition, music trance, or simple focus are all included in the field of meditation. If the concept of sitting still, breathing, and quieting the mind seems unattainable, try doing something you love with extreme focus. This intense focus will bring attention to the present moment and generate mindfulness. This mindfulness is crucial to the healing of your child. Whether it is applied to emotional evaluation, critical self-talk, or eating-awareness, mindfulness leads to a deeper sense of understanding. When your child is able to live mindfully, he or she will most likely be able to live happily.

Does This Feel Familiar?

A New Way of Thinking

"Our minds are introduced at a very young age to certain types of media that cause incredible damage, sometimes even irreversible damage. Not only are women in our society faced with the stereotypical look that is thought to represent beauty, we all assume that a life lived by achieving this look would be easier. The myth that many women believe, "you can never be too thin," has caused countless women and girls to fall under the abusive spell of anorexia.

Anorexia is crippling, not only to men and women of our generation but for men and women of the world. Our society strives to be what the world tells us is beautiful but beauty should never be defined by size or become a competition. However, we are the victims of our own crimes. We have allowed our personal views and common sense to be altered by the media we willingly allow ourselves to absorb.

It is critical to find a new way of thinking. Find new creative avenues of healing. Find a way to only hear the truths.

Living around this devouring disease has allowed me to understand its ways from the inside out. This sickness is one that not only affects the victim but engulfs everyone even the slightest bit involved with it. Being in a family that includes someone who is enslaved by this hell has allowed me to understand how powerful and truly corrupting this lifestyle is. My family was unwillingly forced to live side by side with the disease anorexia. Every aspect of our daily lives were affected by it, going out to dinner, having a full-length mirror, keeping secrets from loved ones around us. However, the deepest effect it had on me was struggle to love the victim. I had to learn to recognize that her actions, that limited my life, were a result not of her selfishness of rather of her disease. I also had to fight to stay connected with my other family members amongst tearing pain. The day she left for treatment I realized I would have to be more of a parent to my younger sibling, and more of a comforter for my devastated parents, roles someone at my age should never have to fill. I learned that many families that live with disease will live with it for forever. However, my family somehow found the strength to work together to become whole again, to be a family again.

Survival, although thought to be impossible, I know now is more than achievable. I have watched first hand, over the past six years, my family take anorexia down with love and forgiveness. I have developed a passion to help others learn to love themselves, to see their bodies as beautiful, just as they were created. We have to stop believing what we are fed by the media and find new, novel and radical ways to not only hear . . . but to believe in the truths."

– A Child Who Witnessed the Lies of Anorexia

NOTES

NOTES

NOTES

NOTES

WHAT'S THE BIGGER PICTURE?

"Maybe thinking of others before/equal to yourself is the most effective medicine for the unending abuse. For it is hard to hate yourself when you feel connected to another. The amount of time spent obsessing over perfection could be spent being a lover. A friend. An advocate. A daughter. A wife. A sister. A blessing. A teacher. A student. An ally. A researcher. A helper. A caretaker. A giver. An artist. A change-maker. That time is precious. Once given away, it will never come back. So here is my Thomas Edison, my invention, my thought. Let me not get caught in the web of lies being fed to me by a media rooted in insecurity. Let my mind be filled with power, might, creativity, and love versus impurity. For every minute I waste trying to perfect myself is a minute less that I could have chosen heaven over hell."

– Diary Entry

14 SERVICE TO OTHERS

[
"The best way to find yourself is to lose yourself
in the service of others."
— Mahatma Gandhi[57]
]

Service to others and/or volunteer work is most often effective with eating-disorder patients after work has been done to restore brain chemistry, and the body is no longer malnourished. A starving body needs food, and as a result, the clairvoyance of the brain will begin to follow. For many of us, at this point of recovery a mom can help focus and/or re-focus on service work. Without this refocus, the service work becomes about the disease.

With almost all other mental illnesses, we use exercise as a way to refocus with a flow of serotonin and healthy bodies. This is not possible with eating disorders, and thus makes service work a possible choice. The brain is able to refocus away from the eating disorder and on to something else. This is when a caretaker can create opportunities for the child to find someone or something to

57. Larry Chang. *Wisdom for the Soul: Five Millenia of Prescriptions ofr Spiritual Healing.* Gnosophia Publishers. 2006. Print. 626.

serve other than her/himself.

Once your child is stable, when the brain is nourished and the body is safe from medical danger, is a great time to start volunteer work. Service work is often a frustrating waste of time if your child is not mentally ready, and you do not want to introduce another feeling of failure. The service needs to be a good fit, and the child needs to be invested in what they are doing, thus avoiding the feelings of failure or a potential relapse.

Although we recommend service work after the brain is stable, we have also witnessed successes when introducing service work early in the diagnosis. Repetition of experiences builds neural pathways in the brain; this is truest if your family is service-oriented. Let's be honest. All mothers are service-oriented from the time their child is born. Wondering "when to start serving" leaves you with the "chicken before the egg" question, as there is no perfect time to start. When to begin volunteer/service work is a personal answer, and you as the caretaker/guardian have to decide the timing. Sometimes it's trial and error depending on your experience. Essentially, don't procrastinate. Often it is a commitment that becomes a purposeful pleasure, sparking new experiences and knowledge.

> *"I think repetition affects the neural pathways and it is most effective combined with cognitive behavioral therapy. When the service fit is right it gives the child a feeling of positively participating in the world and a break from the selfishness of the eating disorder. Think sometimes that initial selflessness has to be forced, positive feelings are inevitable when helping someone or something else and then brain chemistry changes."*
>
> – Mom of Four

We have heard it since we were children: "you receive more than you give." It's a simple but well-documented statement that has survived the test of time. Think of it as interchangeable goodness! You, your child, your family, and those you aid will benefit.

What Could a Mom Do Now?

Inquire and learn about what service opportunities are available in your community. There will be something your community needs that will be available and interesting for your child. Ask the school counselor, your place of worship, and friends in the neighborhood for referrals. Check the internet for listings.

Why is Service to Others Important?

- Service to others is service to self.
- Service creates a more compassionate way of living.
- Service can alleviate the pain of personal torment—both exposing and validating the dichotomy of human existence. You are never alone in suffering.
- Service opens the door to a myriad of human emotions, some joyful and some sad. It's that exposure that helps you grow as a person. The experience empowers both yourself and others.
- It is you who repairs, reconciles, expands, and hopefully finds a greater purpose than what we materialistically desire.
- It is time well spent.
- Service provides global comfort. The up-and-coming generation lives globally, and the sooner we expose our children to the needs of their world, the better equipped

they will be as global citizens.

- Service can increase self-confidence, combat depression, build relationships, and bring fulfillment and fun into your life.

- Service will enhance your current skill set and expand your knowledge.

- Volunteer jobs, though not paid, can teach new job skills and introduce you to new and potential fields of career opportunities.

- It helps one to be less judgmental and more tolerant as you work side by side in new and unexpected relationships.

- It builds self-confidence. You are worthy, purposeful, and needed by other people.

"Service to others has allowed me to grow, to learn and to strengthen my personal understanding of the world. I'm in college and appreciate the gift of an education and yet, the gift of experiential hands-on learning is just as important to my personal understanding of humanity. At this point I have been volunteering since I was a little girl and I am able to reflect back on experiences and see my own self-worth, my reason for being here and recognize I am important. We all are important. Service work has taught me to become part of the bigger picture rather than becoming focused only on my life. It has broadened my views and has been a stepping stone for me to get involved in the lives of other people. This has created space for me to love others and through that learn to love myself."

– A Social Work Student

Find the Right Fit

Service does not always include physical manpower, but it does include the way you choose to live your life every day! Sometimes so-called service is as easy as everyday kindness.

If you and your child are not ready to engage in hands-on volunteer work, do not force a commitment. Instead be open to creatively forging a different service path. For example:

- Adopt a child in a different country who you are required to write once a month. It is a commitment.
- Work at the Society for Prevention of Cruelty to Animals (SPCA) with animals enhancing physical, calming, and loving touch.
- Write a letter to a government agency, your school, and/ or your place of worship on behalf of a belief or idea you feel passionate about. Lobby for good.
- Write letters to veterans and soldiers.
- Spend time with the elderly. Offer to teach and use technology. And most importantly, just be there and listen to them.
- Use social media to spread the word on positive, newsworthy causes. Utilizing social media is important because it is prevalent to our children's way of life, but it is also easy to become obsessed with no accountability. Please be careful and wise when choosing a social media outlet; eating disorders are compulsive in behavior, and you don't want to amplify the problems.

Build Your Village of Support

Volunteering takes personal time and emotional energy, and it can be scary to be out of your comfort zone. Try your best to be consistent and committed. Provide the opportunity for relationships and their growth. When you have relationships you cannot just focus on yourself. This is particularly true for people struggling with eating disorders. Healthy relationships are a critical part of healing.

When people from various backgrounds gather to work from the heart, relationships are built on passion, often creating lifelong friendships. Working for good brings out the best in you and the best in others, and together, in the same mindset of love and service, we actually can change the world for better.

Volunteering broadens your village, finding commonality with others of different backgrounds, religions, and political views. The common goals unite a diverse community. Passion gifts you with joy and love, two of the most meaningful human emotions.

Working together for good is a spiritual experience; it moves people beyond the thoughts of self into an understanding of deity and goodness. Service helps you realize it actually is possible to feel like an instrument of peace.

> *"Lord, make me an instrument of Thy peace.*
> *Where there is hatred, let me sow love.*
> *Where there is injury, pardon.*
> *Where there is doubt, faith.*
> *Where there is despair, hope.*
> *Where there is darkness, light.*
> *Where there is sadness, joy..."*
> – St. Francis of Assisi[58]

58. "Prayer of Saint Francis." Catholic Online.. Web. 09 Nov. 2016. www.catholic.org/prayers.

Be an Example

Are you already philanthropy-oriented? Be an example to your child. When appropriate, invite your child and family to join you. Your volunteerism can be a crucial piece of your own healing. It gets you out of the eating-disorder obsession, and when you choose to be openhearted, you broaden your thinking and experiences. Leading by example helps you become a stronger person. Remember, you affect those you are closest to by just being you.

> *"O Divine Master: grant that I may not so much seek to be consoled as to console: to be understood as to understand: to be loved as to love: for it is in giving that we receive."*
> – St. Francis of Assisi[59]

Include Your Family

Even if you do not really want to serve and/or if your child (family) fights you all the way there, go anyway. We can promise that, eventually, the act of service imprints positivity upon your heart and memory. The positive feelings help shape a more favorable view of yourself, the world, and others. It gives one the ability to sympathize and experience empathy for human beings, thus living beyond your own selfish desires. So volunteer for fun, for service hours, to make connections, or any reason at all, and eventually your child, your family, and you will feel the passion.

In this book, we have used the word "lonely" many times. Caretaking a loved one with an eating disorder is lonely. Caretaking in general can be challenging. By serving those less fortunate

---

59. "Prayer of Saint Francis." Catholic Online.. Web. 09 Nov. 2016. www.catholic.org/prayers.

(and no matter how bad your life seems, there are always others in worse condition), you are given the opportunity to make a choice on how you view life. This is not to undermine your troubles but to recognize that all people have struggles, and each struggle is relative to that life. Are you able to be grateful? Are you able to empathize with others? Are you able to steer your thinking and mood toward realistic hope? Are you optimistic? Are you caught in the vicious cycle of obsession with the eating disorder? If you are, you are normal! All of us have been sucked in by the grip of our child's/loved one's eating disorder, and it is lonely. It can be very depressing. But what did we do? We broadened our minds and moods by volunteering. Sometimes our children and families joined us, and sometimes we ventured out on our own. Sometimes it was just a day at the shelter serving hot meals, and for some of us, it is our lives' work.

The point is, go and do something for someone else. Give freely and lovingly of yourself without the expectation of rewards or results. We believe that your life will be brighter with success defined by meaning. You will feel better about yourself, and when you love yourself, you will be a better parent, friend, family member, and/or co-worker.

Soul Food

"Give because giving feeds the soul. Give because in helping others you help yourself. Because in the act of giving, the focus on self is removed. This shift then allows you to dedicate your attention to others. In turn, your heart and soul are touched and opened and you can see deep within yourself. Giving requires a non-judgmental open heart and mind.

To look into the eyes of a homeless man, hold the hand of an orphaned child or share a meal with a family that barely makes ends meet, is humbling beyond words. Seeing. Feeling. Touching others allows you the opportunity to view life through a different lens. Others could be the less fortunate or it could be your own child. Seeing our child through a new lens, a perspective you never knew existed or could even imagine. I think that in the recovery process, there probably comes a time when giving would become a great form of therapy.

More often than not, one realizes the people you are "helping" have more than you do. They possess grace, hope, faith and the belief that everything will be OK. They have enough and that is all any of us needs. Enough.

So make the opportunity to give a priority in your life, in your recovery. Maybe the giving is right here in your own backyard or half way around the world in a country and a culture you know nothing about. It does not matter! Each of us has the ability to get out of our comfort zone, open our heart, extend our hand and make a difference. I promise in the giving you will receive more than you ever dreamed possible.

Find your tiny corner of the world and make a difference in just one life. Because the life of that one person affects the lives of many, and will grow and strengthen you like nothing else in this world can."

– A Mom and Child Appointed Court Advocate

Look back into history at those who left this world a better place. Those marks were not made without helping others in need—often with pain and suffering, but always with extensive giving and inevitable receiving. Every religion across this planet asks you to "help take care of others" by loving your neighbor as yourself; it is said in the Torah, the Hindu Vedas, the Bible, the Koran, Bahá'í, Buddhism, Taoism, Confucianism, and more. Every moral and honorable principal is based on giving to others.

Service provides the invaluable possibilities that money cannot buy: contentment, meaningful relationships, gift of giving, receiving, love, passion, connection, and purpose. A life beyond yourself can improve your health, your mental state, and your happiness.

Please give service/volunteerism a fair try. There is never an ideal time to begin and/or continue, but you will know when it is right. You will feel a difference in your existence. Give service to others a fair chance; that is all you can ask of yourself.

> *"I slept and dreamt that life was joy. I awoke and saw that life was service. I acted and behold, service was joy."*
> – Rabindranath Tagore[60]

Does This Feel Familiar?

Two Versions of Myself!

"How is it that there are currently two people living in my home that have never experienced running water, are truly illiterate, and have never had enough

---

60. Tagore, Rabindranath. "I Slept and Dreamt That Life Was Joy." N.p., n.d. Web. www. projecthappiness.com

food yet all I can manage to think about is how much I don't want to eat. How could I possibly be willing to starve myself when there are people who have literally been starved based on poverty and not privilege? How could I be so selfish? How could I succumb to this level of vanity?

I remember these thoughts echoing through my mind constantly during the time in which my parents chose to invite a Haitian family to live in our home with us. My parents had very intentionally chosen this time to host the family, as I was in the midst of an eating disorder—in desperate need for purpose outside of my addiction and a commonality that didn't revolve around the brokenness my illness was causing.

I am forever grateful that my generous parents were so willing and so courageous to serve when it was anything but convenient. They were the most beautiful examples of what it meant to truly love without condition and what genuine generosity looked like.

My brother and sister were incredible as well. Intentionality came so easy to them. They were able to connect with the family right off the bat and were eager to forgo birthday parties, plans with friends, and their personal pleasures to ensure that the family staying with us was always more comfortable than they were. True examples of servants—they were able to gain worldly wisdom and perspective with such ease.

This was not the case for me. You see, I was caught between two versions of myself. It wasn't that I didn't want to be like my siblings—generous, kind, and selfless—it was that I wanted that but I also wanted my addiction. And you can't have both. I always had the logic to understand that my choices were selfish and that my reasoning behind my eating disorder was flawed. However, the need to control would override my desire to be the best version of myself, which led me to end up in a cyclical pattern of bad decision-making leading to negative self-perception.

Service in the midst of an eating disorder can be one of the trickiest subjects of all. It is absolutely critical. However, it is also absolutely dependent upon one's willingness to forgo their selfish tendencies . . . and there are few things in the world that cause selfishness more than addiction and this type of disease. It is not that we are selfish people at heart . . . it is that the disease causes us to act selfishly and to have selfish thoughts. At times, it can even feel as if we have no control at all over our inability to think outside of our own minds. We are held captive to the mental monster we are serving and we are unable to escape.

In order to truly serve we must be willing to get outside of our own perspective. We must become the person we were meant to be; the person we want to be. You see, within each of us is a deep desire to have purpose. And I have found that purpose most often comes in the form of helping another. We crave this. And quite frankly we need this. We are desperate for it.

That is why service is so crucial to recovery and healing. It gives us purpose. It reminds us of who we want to be and ensures us that the person we want to be is the person we are meant to be. Without service, we stay captive to the voice in our head that keeps us chained to self-loathing and hatred.

In the beginning we might only get to a place where we are torn. A place where we are only able to see the irrational thinking going on in our clouded minds. However, I can speak from experience, slowly but surely, through the practice of service, incredible healing occurs. Those two versions of yourself slowly morph into one clear vision, one clear purpose. The confusion and frustration transforms into a willingness to let go of the vanity and to show up as the human we are made to be."

– A Twenty-Four-Year-Old Who is Now Service-Oriented

15 FAITH PRACTICES

[We all need a place to put our hope.]

Religion is everything, and religion is nothing. Religion is life, and religion is death. Religion exists beyond the confines of humanity, for it is a practice of the spirit. No amount of words, action, thought, feeling, or belief can capture its true essence. It is unformed, ever-changing, ever-evolving beyond the confines of human experience and perception.

We all need an explanation for the unexplainable. We all need a place to put our hope. We cannot put our "faith" in a person; they eventually pass on, structures break, and the tangible will diminish with time. Everything on earth that we tend to put faith in is temporary. We all desire to have faith in something that is good, that cannot be taken away. It's an anthropological concept that mankind has always searched for "God." Civilizations of past and present use "God" to explain their existence and the world around them. Through the wonderment of miracles and the excruciating hardships in our lives, we question, Is there something more?

Have you ever felt this desire for more, asked yourself, *Is there something bigger?* Have you ever wondered about a Higher Power that can only be personified in language, with words describing an understanding beyond our current human capacity? The life of everyone present, past, and future is personally designed such that no two people on this earth are the exact same. Though we are not exactly alike, our desire to love and be loved is the profound common similarity that bonds us in this life as a member of the human race. We are wonderfully flawed, diverse people who search and expand themselves physically, mentally, and spiritually like never before, but we still need more. And it is those common similarities that have bonded us throughout out all of history and proven over and over again a natural desire for something greater—a God beyond our own will and understanding.

We get glimpses of this Higher Power through great teachers—Jesus, Buddha, and Mohammed. Sometimes those teachers are our own children, our friends, or a stranger. Every individual has to find his or her own path to this Higher Power of love and hope.

For some, it takes loneliness, doubt, and sometimes pain to spark the desire in the depths of our being to search for that "more." For others, it is those moments of silence, joy, or laughter when we recognize its existence. This so-called "more" is felt and recognized by each human in a different way through different mediums and experiences.

As for our loved one's struggle with an eating disorder, this humanistic desire for "more" is often hidden or overshadowed by the disease's desire for "more me." As a result of the disease's negativity, it is natural for our loved ones to search for self-worth in earthly things or through the approval of society. But it will never be found, no matter how thin, rich, smart, pretty, or athletic our loved one is.

"Within us there is an inner, natural dignity. (You often see it in older folks.) An inherent worthiness that already knows and enjoys. (You see it in children.) It is an immortal diamond waiting to be mined and is never discovered undesired. It is a reverence humming within us that must be honored. Call it the True Self, the soul, the unconscious, deep consciousness, or the indwelling Holy Spirit. Call it nothing. It does not need the right name or right religion to show itself. It does not even need to be understood. It is usually wordless. It just is, and it shows itself best when we are silent, or in love, or both. It is God-in-All-Things yet not circumscribed by any one thing. It is enjoyed only when each part is in union with all other parts, because only then does it stand in the full truth." [61]

— Richard Rohr

Children with eating disorders struggle with a lack of significance and worthiness. As caretakers, can we provide an example of that unconditional love here on earth? Molding a faith practice can help us with that. In order to recover from an eating disorder, one must have a sense of purpose and perspective in life. These qualities are often most effectively cultivated through a spiritual practice of sorts. No matter if the practice is labeled a "religion," a "way of life," or simply a "world perspective," the spiritual element of recovery plays a critical role in healing as well as a crucial role in preventing relapse later down the road.

No matter your religious preference or cultural heritage, we believe a faith practice is critical to recovery.

---

61. Rohr, Richard. *Immortal Diamond: The Search for Our True Self.* Goyang: Korean Institute of the Christian Studies, 2015. Print.

"Faith is a root component that if not carefully attended to may show symptoms in other areas of our lives. I believe faith can be a healing part of every human being. It's definitely not the only part, and needs to be attended to carefully. I've never seen faith heal a broken arm. I've never seen faith regrow a missing appendage. I've never seen faith work someone out of depression, at least without the careful guidance of professional psychiatrist or psychologist. But I have seen faith begin to give hope, and often times hope is an unquantifiable salve to help heal the mind and the body."

– Andy Braner, President KIVU
Gap Year and Author

We all have had moments when we feel the presence of the Holy Spirit at a gospel church, on a mountain top, in an orphanage of abandoned children, in the call to prayer, a shared Shabbat dinner, at the river's edge, the death bed of a loved one, the birth of a child, or at the foot of the cross. The practice of faith comes in actively seeking those places, and that place looks different for everyone. You have to find where the veil of God is the thinnest and go there.

"The spiritual Journeyman is invited into a self-examination of awareness. No matter what system of religion you choose each has a unique way of inviting the individual into a place where the self isn't the only part of connecting to the world. Often there is a higher power, or a higher

being of creation that gives us the freedom to exist in our "true-self." And specifically with a mental illness stigma, it's important to find places where we are allowed to be who we are. It's no one's fault we struggle with depression, eating disorders, or suffer with bi-polar. Many times we can find chemical imbalances that can begin to be treated with proper medication. And if we can find networks inside faith communities able to accept humankind as proper image bearers of a creator, we can find social healing to work in tandem with physical healing.

It becomes an issue of addressing the "whole" human, rather than simply trying to treat one symptom to move on to another. Human beings aren't like any other part of our world today. We can't simply change the oil, rotate the tires, and change the timing belts and be on our way. Human beings need holistic ways of looking at the world to climb their way to healing. Faith communities can provide one part."

– Andy Braner, President KIVU
Gap Year and Author

Can we, as mothers, help our children find those places?

Spiritual practices keep you focused on a power higher than yourself. The worship offers a sense of purpose, perspective, and love to practitioners. Sometimes that purpose derives from service to others while other times it is reflected in the development of one's compassion. Spiritual practices come in a wide variety of forms: reading sacred religious texts, meditation, prayer, journaling, chanting, spiritual ceremonies, and communal gatherings. Any act that causes one to feel a connection to God is spiritual.

The act is less important than the experience it evokes. When spiritual practices are effective, experiences of peace, love, and acceptance often occur. Anything that allows us to sense the presence of the Divine brings healing and transformation—the hope of healing that brings us out of the darkest of places.

A deep sense of purpose is not often found in those struggling with an eating disorder. Whether the purpose has been replaced with disordered eating, or whether the individual never had a strong sense of purpose in the first place is irrelevant. The restoration of purpose can be found through spirituality. When a sense of purpose is attained outside of body goals or physical appearance, a different type of healing occurs. Purpose is redefined for the individual, and self-worth can be restored. Connection to that which is greater than ourselves allows us to feel purposeful and valued.

Matthew Williams is a trauma counselor who restores hope and life in child soldiers in the Congo. Consider his insight.

"I have met and/or counseled few, if any, individuals who dismissed the need for or longing for something transcendent (most often a loving God) when faced with the overwhelming. That "overwhelming" may be the result of an eating disorder, war trauma, abuse, or insert any number of overwhelming circumstances. Faced with such, we humans often recognize (even if for the first time) our need for a higher power, a loving God, or a transcendent purpose. Few have expressed this more poignantly that Viktor Frankl, author of "Man's Search for Meaning." And few can question his qualifications to speak to the need of, dare I say, every human for "self-transcendence." A professor

of neurology and psychiatry, Frankl was also a survivor of four, WW2 concentration camps. Bearing witness to death and life . . . to horrid traumas and selfless courage, Frankl wrote about a key, common denominator in those who bravely faced the worst of conditions, endured suffering with dignity, and ultimately survived. That common denominator he called «the self-transcendence of human existence"—that is, a transcendent purpose great-er/more purposeful than one's mere existence. Living for one's self provides no grand motivation to live . . . much less to overcome. Yet to live with love for another or to find hope in something greater . . . that can empower individuals to overcome the most overwhelming of odds. It may even have the power to restore the psyche—the soul, mind, spirit; breath; life."

– Matthew Williams, MA, Counselor and
Director of Operations of Exile International

Gaining perspective is another component of a spiritual practice. Most practices bring attention to the whole of humanity and the universe. When the mind is filled with a perspective outside of the limited self-perspective, it is able to alter thought, patterns, and beliefs. This type of alteration proves highly beneficial, if not essential, in recovery from an eating disorder. When an individual struggling with an eating disorder is able to "get outside their own mind," he or she is then able to view the world with different lenses. Spiritual practices are the lenses by which perspective can be shifted. The nature of an eating disorder is to trick the mind into existing only within the limited self-perspective. However, through the implementation of a spiritual practice, one is able to gain insight into an alternate viewpoint and move towards a transformation of beliefs and thoughts.

Through these practices and the attainment of purpose and perspective, one becomes better acquainted with practices of love as well. Almost all religions and spiritual disciplines emphasize the importance for love for others and love for the self. This concept is critical in recovery. As spirituality leads to a deeper sense of love, it also leads to a gentleness and acceptance that has been lacking in the life of your child.

This final chapter is a different format. We are not going to give suggestions on "What Could a Mom Do Now?" Faith is so personal to one's existence that you have to explore and answer your own questions.

There is a reason many recovery programs are faith-based and focused on God and their understanding of a Higher Power.

"It feels important to encourage the faith of a person without the religious, man-made, fence-lines. We've bastardized the essence of conviction, something that comes natural to human beings. We have just simply insulted the "truths."

As we embrace others and cross-cultural boundaries, all of us have to learn mutual respect focusing the similarities in our intangible beliefs that are the undercurrent for all that exist. It's the happenings, notions, events, feelings, thoughts of all that we do not control that cause so much worry in our unsettled souls. So much we will never control. One of the most common traits of an eating disorder is the control issue. Actually, the lack thereof. In the end, we actually control little and must learn to rely on an inner peace that surpasses all understanding. This is so hard for those who struggle to give up control. Can be so difficult to rely on the gift of breath as and use coping skills learned for relaxation. Gratitude helps reduce anxiety. Faith cultivates gratitude. Helping each other tap into our own personal faith and truth is paramount to recovery and to daily living.

I have touched it, felt it, and experienced the unusual, and it's crucial to the restfulness, quiet, and insight of one's own soul thus all our brothers and sisters. I do not believe this is a learned behavior but rather that internal knowledge. One has to be open to tap into the image in which we were created."

– A Mom

For many of us, faith communities have been deeply healing. We had to be diligent about nurturing our faith, making time to pray, meditate, commune, read, and breathe. If you do not currently connect with a faith, perhaps it is time to take the first step forward in finding your place of worship. The truths and convictions within faith strengthen the human core. So much of parenting comes from within the human core. The human core is an extension of our soul. We have a physical body, but we are the soul. Mystery lies within our soul—that powerful place of wonderment from which we live. Our soul is home to the Divine Holy Spirit.

Does This Feel Familiar?

It Is Well

"Lots of people know this familiar hymn first published in 1876. You may have seen the quote "It Is Well" in the written word as uplifting wisdom or soft consoling words in times of despair. You might even see it as a tattoo on a twenty-something's body! But most people do not know this hymn was written following a series of deep traumas endured by Spafford, the most painful being the death of his young son.

When my friend (the mother whose child had fought a nasty eating disorder) asked me to consider writing a piece on faith, I hesitated. "Oh gosh, I'm not a good writer, my story is to deep and perplexing . . ." But quickly, I realized my story is your story, our pain is shared in the human heart, we are all very similar and the pain of love has a common pattern. The author of this timeless hymn knew that together, by the Grace of God, he teaches us to find peace. So, please let me tell you why "it is well with my soul" even in the face of pain and suffering.

On a calm summer evening a car of teenagers, going eighty miles an hour with their lights off, hit my fiancée's car. He died twice on the emergency room table that night and ended up in a coma. That was twenty-eight years ago; today my husband has a traumatic brain injury that affects every part of his life. We know now that when he did finally wake from his coma after four weeks, the beginning of a hard daily journey was just starting with the reality of work beginning with twelve months of inpatient physical rehab. My husband was never going to be the same. Unlike the final scene of a movie where the protagonist walks out of the hospital healed, well . . . our new reality was not a fairy tale. Life would be challenging. He would have to learn how to walk, use a fork, read, write, cloth himself and talk again. He has paralysis on his right side, aphasia, cognitive difficulties, executive functioning difficulties, and difficulty controlling his behavior. After six months of therapy, the counselor advised counseling to learn to care for a loved one with a life-long illness. At twenty, you have no idea what that really means!

We married a year after the accident and it was quite the celebration of life, family and FAITH. Yes, faith, because it was my faith that lead me to continue our relationship from engaged to married. At twenty-three you have no idea what that really means. He had to have help with his vows, help walking down the aisle, and assistance at the reception. I had no idea that this was just the beginning. I had no idea the emotional toil that caring for a loved one was going to bring.

It broke me, crushed my dreams, frustrated me and I was tired. Really tired. But the good Lord had a different idea about the future! I had the burden of financially supporting our family and after seven years of work decided to start my own company. A bold leap of faith! Yet, not sure how life was going to play out! (Fast forward to 2016, I could go on and on and on about my work and how it has sustained me. Not because of the actual work but because it is a source of plugging into others' lives, praying for others, encouraging others, teaching younger peeps, is a gift to me! It fuels me and has provided our family a way to live that I never dreamed.)

During the next seven years of therapy, we began to accept the things that would not be changing. My husband made progress but his hand was not going to work. His experimental surgeries did not work. We learned how to live with in the reality of his injury. It was much easier to accept the physical difficulties than the mental/ behavioral parts. It has been helpful that he has an incredible attitude for life. He always wants to be with others, to laugh, to plug in, to help others, to be involved, a faith that everything is going to be all right. It has served him well.

Blessed with parents who loved God, the teachings of the Lord were part of our daily lives; normal and real. But this "normal and real faith" became my lifeline; a necessity for my sanity and survival. In my mind, there was no option but to rely on Him, trust Him enough to gain mental and emotional strength beyond my human capacity. I now realize He was preparing me for far harder circumstances that would come.

The next three-and-a-half years were a complete blur. We were blessed with three sons in a short amount of time. They were precious, healthy, so much fun and an absolute joy. They replaced my loneliness, the love of a child can do that. Even though I was very girly growing up, I learned for the first time in my thirties to play baseball, to catch a football, to play airsoft guns, and to teach boys to wakeboard. And yet, I battled a lingering guilt about the amount of time work demanded and the balance was challenging. I had a flexible schedule. I could help the kids and my husband more. I could pay the bills. My mind was being stimulated. It was a win-win. But, I was not able to do it alone. My parents, brother and sister-in-law were constantly helping us raise our children. It felt well with my soul; I was forever grateful for their love and support.

But imperfectly fallible, I would fall out of balance and began sinking again. An older female friend suggested I drop the guilt and look at life as a blessing, I was provided for. He was providing. I began getting help for myself. I started going to a counselor. I wanted someone to make things normal in our marriage and the balance of motherhood, work and life smooth. The professionals kept telling me that I was on a slow simmer and my top was going to blow off. But how do you stop a simmer when your top hasn't blown off? Things were working ok. I could put on a smile, kiss away tears, work full time, keep up with the chores, cook a yummy dinner, keep my kids happy, send them to a Christian school, take them to church. I could control my world as best as I knew how. Was it really well with my soul? At times it was but not always. He was, yet again, preparing me for far harder circumstances that would come.

Our youngest, a high-energy child, had three back-to-back head injuries. All requiring trauma, and hospitalizations transferred by ambulance and/ or Care Flight. (That is another story!) After the third accident, I remember sitting in the parking lot crying to my sister-in-law. "How are we going to do this?" Fear set in, panic set in. Protecting our children is a maternal instinct that is overwhelming. When their well-being is out of our control fear takes hold. God was, yet again, preparing me for far harder circumstances that would come.

Our oldest son started using drugs and alcohol when he was fourteen. Darling, friendly, outgoing, this boy was the one that always shared his life with me. I enjoy his company so much. Friendships started changing, he started changing. A mom will go to desperate measures to change a terrifying situation for their child. We went to a counselor on a regular basis but the learning did not happen. Instead, more abuse. Until, it was normal. Vodka, a six-pack, a DUI, an MIP and a daily high, treatment centers, family therapy, psychological testing, evading arrest, homelessness, suicide attempt and six constant years of anguish.

It was such a difficult time and those of you who know about substance abuse understand its wicked ways of destruction. For a parent, I wonder if eating disorders and mental illness harvest the same fearful feelings of losing a child. I think so. The caregiving is similar; boundaries, tough-love, sleepless nights, and consequences require unquantifiable mental strength and lack there-of! The pain of love has a common pattern.

I worried 24/7. Worrying got me nowhere.

I began to get help on a steady basis, Most professionals would say, "What are you doing for yourself?" It took me years to figure out what they meant. Now I get it but it doesn't come naturally. Finally, I made a decision to step out of my comfort zone and went on mission trip to Africa with my two youngest boys. This might sound cliché in the era of the millennial, but it was extraordinary and changed a profound understanding in my life of experience. God was, yet again, preparing me. Not for harder circumstances to come but for a higher understanding that connects us all.

A constant reminder of this harmony is the precious fifteen-year-old girls whose existence, when I first met them, was minimal in a remote African village. Sadly, they knew hell on earth: abuse, prostitution, poverty and little to no support. And yet, it was these young ladies who became my teachers through their big smiles, warm hugs and incomprehensible joy. Where did they get that abounding joy? Their powerful prayers of grace offered up stung me to the core! They lived the hardest lives I have seen to-date and yet, these beautiful souls loved with passion and depth. I have now traveled to other developing countries and often still can't believe it . . . same story! Different country, different culture, often fewer resources but the people love fervently. It was well with their souls. Its had a profound effect on me to think that even in the midst of the saddest times in my life, I too can still keep going, love others, and have joy. The depth of this universal love is not of the earth, it is the joy of faith in something that makes order out of chaos and peace of out anxiety. It offers rest from worry, rest from being in control, rest from fear, rest from the future. "Cast all your anxieties on Him for He cares for you" (1 Peter 5:7 NIV).

Many years have passed and many more chapters to our storybook of life. And guess what? I am still not in control. But, with complete honesty and a realistic outlook on life, I trust my Lord and have so much to be thankful for. I choose to be thankful for my dear friends, family and "village." We have a band of relatives, neighbors, co-workers, and friends that are at our side. I can't say this enough. When in trials, this is a must!!!! It keeps me from being isolated and in my own head. I never knew how important the provision of loving support would be at a young age. I cannot do life without them. In many ways my life requires the same quest for resolution to challenging problems. But, I know I am okay, not alone but saddled in unwavering faith that God is with me. I may have wavered in worry and fear and even checked out at times. I still do. But HE . . . well, not only has He never left, He carries our burden when the weight is too heavy to bear.

Our son is using again so our story is still in progress. So once again, as always, I earnestly rely on the Lord, reach out for help from a therapist, friends and family.

The mental, emotional, and spiritual side of life affects our being much more than the physical. The shared human concerns: parental worry, fear of expectations not being met, loneliness, prayers not answered the way we want them to, resentment, disappointments, failed efforts and/or botched experimental treatments with this or that this doctor. These feelings and emotions led us on a journey that has brought about a lot of hardship. But look closely because, if not right this moment, eventually you experience joy, purpose, and an empathy for others. Our trials and tribulations make the need for others' assistance and the need to plug into others that much richer. And yet there is more. Across the planet mankind continues to search for that peace that surpasses all understanding. Who is the Creator of all? Can I depend upon Him for real? Not only can you, I dare to say, you have to. We are not created to live in solitude. We need each other and we need the one who abides beyond our human comprehension. God is not going away, even when and if everything else does.

Each of us who have felt the pain of loving someone battling addiction, struggling with a mental or physical handicap and/or dealing with mental illness or an eating disorder gets caught in the stress and fear of our own daunting human mind. One day I can handle the same problem, but I fell apart two days prior. The situation was the same but my mind and heart were not. I have to put myself in the face of God and find credence in the spiritual promises not in the human emotion of fear. The faith is there, "my ways are higher than your ways," and though I can only see in three-dimensional moment of time, God comprehends a divine order that exceeds my understanding. Over the decades of life, I have been both blessed and wounded but never alone. He is always faithful.

God gifts us with His strength and the fortitude of others that walk this journey sharing and experience life together. We are not alone and it is so important to draw that inner strength from others, be grounded in our faith and when appropriate, pass it on to others in need. I am grateful for my life. And so, it is the Creator of everything that grants me the peace to feel with my heart and know with my mind, "it is well with my soul."

— A Mom Whose Faith Sustains Her

CLOSING

There Is No Ending to This Book

[The story is yours to continue.]

Your story is intricately unique to you, as it is for your child, your loved ones, and your family.

One of the challenges with eating-disorder recovery and any mental disorder is that the disorder is manipulative and intangible, unlike a medical problem solved with surgery, medication, or physical therapy. Therefore, the journey to recovery is complex and unique.

"Mental illnesses—whatever kind—are so very hard. I honestly have wished my child had cancer sometimes. What mother would ever have such a thought?! But cancer you can cut out, treat with strong meds, and is socially acceptable. Mental illness is sneaky, insidious, and unscrupulous.

Friends and family understand cancer. It is tangible; you can see a tumor, test blood for bad cells. Treatment is definitive. You have something specific to fight and everyone can sympathize with a cancer patient. Society does not understand mental illness; it is vague and abstract. Even with as much progress as we have made with eating disorders, they are still misunderstood. It creeps up on individuals and families and makes all of us question who we are and the people we love. Diagnosis is difficult and treatment is multifaceted and never a quick fix.

And yet, there is always hope. Hope for a better tomorrow. With advancements in technology, psychology and neuroscience it is my hope that one day soon it will be us, the human being, that imprisons mental illness instead of us being its prisoner.

I truly believe that every child/person afflicted with an eating disorder or any other mental illness has very special gifts to share with the world. It is our job as mothers, fathers, family friends, as a part of the human race to see these gifts and help our loved ones identify and use them."

– A Mom

If you have fought for your child's life due to an eating disorder or mental illness, you understand the above testimony. When we are brutally honest, every one of us has thought the same thing: *Can't this please be an illness fixed with surgery or drugs?* Currently, there is no easy fix for an eating disorder with surgery or an exact drug, but there is hope for healing. There is always hope for healing.

The inter-strength of families is similar to the intricate entangled root system of aspen trees: Above ground the trees can be scorched, weathered, burnt, poisoned, and visually destroyed, but the complicated, tangled-up, undefeatable root system sprouts again, and the beautiful trees grow larger than ever before. The reason and genius of diligent rebirth cannot be seen. The aspen grove always grows back.

How do we know that healing really is attainable? We know because many of our children are the proof. It may look different for each of them, and yet they share the healing quality of self-love. Loving themselves has set them free to love others and live a fulfilling life.

By tapping into the knowledge of professionals and from learning from all of us—moms, dads, brothers, sisters, aunts, uncles, and grandparents—we pray you are better equipped to move forward in helping yourself and your family.

There is a universal desire to see all eating disorders and mental illness cured—not just healed, but vanished, as in totally gone away forever. Is that possible? We don't know, but it is a goal worth working towards.

During the worst and darkest times of life is when we learned the most about ourselves and humanity. Going through the inevitable pain in life is when we discovered our potential and our gifts. Being the mother of a child with an eating disorder is not a road of choice nor a "club" we choose to be in, but we are in that club. And until there is a cure, we will continue the fight. Is it not our jobs as mothers, fathers, family members, friends, as a part of the human race to see the gifts granted through suffering and help our loved ones identify and use those gifts for good? Help our loved ones heal? Help them learn the ultimate earthly gift of being loved, giving love, and loving ourselves, our exquisite human selves?

Thank you for taking the time to read this book. From the bottom of our hearts, we pray this book has helped you know the fight is worth it—that not only are you never alone in this struggle, but you also are capable and competent. You are never perfect, and sometimes wrong, but always perfectly human. The possibilities integrating honesty, love, kindness, and the commitment to doing the best we can do offer the potential for full and comprehensive healing. Ask for help, learn from the professionals, and use us as your learning curve. As we said before, it may not be the exact picture of healing you painted in your mind, with all edges straight and no blended overlap of color. But you will know, you will feel, and you will be deeply grateful. You will confidently be able to answer, "What does it feel like to be the mother of a child with an eating disorder?" You will simply turn to them and say, "Is there anything I can help you with?"

With that said, it feels appropriate and most important to leave you with this last poem written by a survivor to all those who are fighting the battle or witnessing the struggle.

Watch Out Girl...I'm Coming For You

"Watch out girl… I'm coming for you.

I'm coming to adore you so hard that you will never again think that the cellulite on your thigh is anything less than the markings of a goddess or that the rolls on your tummy are not the story of a life fearlessly and courageously enjoyed. When you look in the mirror you will want to yell THANK YOU because you will no longer see a body but a soul . . . and you have a hell of a lot to thank it for.

I am coming to tell you the truth of your magnificence, to erase the lies you used to believe in and replace them with the honesty of your importance, worth, ability, and sheer force.

I am coming to grab you and wrap you in my arms so

tight that you will never EVER feel alone again. Because you are female and to be female is to be one with all. WE are a force to be reckoned with . . . you have a fierce army as your tribe.

I am coming to kiss your precious throat and to remind you that your voice . . . it MATTERS. Your story, your thoughts, your opinions . . . yes. They are the words that are going to heal this aching world. So scream them at the top of your lungs. Be loud and show up.

I am coming to beg for that well of intelligence inside your complicated brain. There is an entire world inside of you just waiting to be unlocked, explored, and discovered. It is just waiting to be tapped into. Never underestimate what you have to offer . . . it is millions of years old and barely born. It is freshly unthought of and also soaked in wisdom. Listen to yourself . . . you have a universe in there.

I am coming to crack open that worried heart of yours. I am going to break it so much that every ounce of intuition, service, wisdom, care, compassion, and goodness is made known to you. You will never again use the words "not enough" because that is no longer your name. You don't even know her.

You will be so overwhelmed with the goodness you find in there that you will take on a new name. You will be called Healed. You will be called A Beautiful Mess. You will be called Imperfect. You will be called Generous. You will be called Capable. You will be called Warrior. You will be called Complicated. And you will own it ALL. You will wear every name for you are everything ...

...so watch out girl cause I'm coming for you."

Signed,
Your Recovered Self

NOTES

NOTES

NOTES

NOTES

APPENDIX

Foreword written by Betty K. Armstrong, Ph.D.
Dr. Armstrong's training in clinical psychology, her theoretical orientation of behavior analysis, and her over thirty years of experience give her a strong foundation for working with clients who struggle with a wide variety of psychological problems: depression, anxiety, relationship conflicts, eating disorders, and emotional traumas. Everyone in the family is affected in some way by the person who struggles with a psychological disorder. Dr. Armstrong's extensive understanding of psychological problems, particularly eating disorders, enhances her ability to offer support, education, and therapy to family members."

www.dr-armstrong.com

————————————————————————— Chapter 1

The following are the four primary eating disorders discussed in this book:

- Anorexia Nervosa (AN)
- Bulimia Nervosa (BN)
- Binge-eating Disorder (BED)

- Other Specified Feeding and Eating Disorders (OSFED)

For definitions of all eating disorders please refer to: **Families Empowered and Supporting Treatment of Eating Disorders (F.E.A.S.T.) Eating Disorder Glossary.** "This glossary is copyright by F.E.A.S.T., an international non-profit organization helping families and caregivers of individuals with eating disorders. We invite eating disorders associations, institutions and treatment providers around the world to link their websites to our glossary for free."

www.glossary.feast-ed.org

...

For diagnostic criteria by the American Psychiatric Association, Diagnostic and Statistical Manual of Mental Disorders (DSMV), visit the website of **The American Psychiatric Association**.

www.psychiatry.org/patients-families/eating-disorders/
what-are-eating-disorders

...

"There has been an unprecedented growth of eating-disordered individuals in the last two decades. Up to 95 percent of those suffering are between the ages of twelve and twenty-six." **The National Eating Disorder Association (NEDA)**.

www.nationaleatingdisorders.org

...

"In reality, no ethnic, gender or socioeconomic group is immune to the dangers of this disease. In regards to gender, 1.5 in 10 cases of these disorders involve males." **The National Association of Anorexia Nervosa and Associated Disorders (ANAD)**.

www.anad.org

——————————————————————— **Chapter 2**

Decoding Anorexia: How Breakthroughs in Science Offer Hope for Eating Disorders
Carrie Arnold 2012

"*Decoding Anorexia* is the first and only book to explain anorexia nervosa from a biological point of view. Its clear, user-friendly descriptions of the genetics and neuroscience behind the disorder is paired with first person descriptions and personal narratives of what biological differences mean to sufferers. Author Carrie Arnold, a trained scientist, science writer, and past sufferer of anorexia, speaks with clinicians, researchers, parents, other family members, and sufferers about the factors that make one vulnerable to anorexia, the neurochemistry behind the call of starvation, and why it's so hard to leave anorexia behind. She also addresses:

- How environment is still important and influences behaviors
- The characteristics of people at high risk for developing anorexia nervosa
- Why anorexics find starvation "rewarding"

- Why denial is such a salient feature, and how sufferers can overcome it

Carrie also includes interviews with key figures in the field who explain their work and how it contributes to our understanding of anorexia. Long thought to be a psychosocial disease of fickle teens, this book alters the way anorexia is understood and treated and gives patients, their doctors, and their family members hope."

www.carriearnold.com

Chapter 3

NCBI Resources: Eating disorder predisposition is associated with ESRRA and HDAC4:

www.ncbi.nlm.nih.gov/pubmed/24216484

...

University of Iowa: Two genes linked to increase risk for eating disorders:

www.now.uiowa.edu/2013/10/two-genes-linked-increased-risk-eating-disorders

...

The Neuroplasticity of the Brain:

www.emilyprogram.com/blog/the-neuroplasticity-of-the-brain

...

Eddie Coker's The Wezmore Project: Supporting young people in honoring their emotional experiences, enhancing psychological resiliency, and encouraging a sense of well-being.

www.thewezmoreproject.com

...

"The role of genetics on Eating Disorders is of particular interest to researchers. Our knowledge at this point indicates that genes load the gun and the environment pulls the trigger." **National Association of Anorexia Nervosa and Associated Disorders (ANAD).**

www.anad.org

...

"*The Parent's Guide to Eating Disorders* by Marcia Herrin is the first book written by a nutritionist that addresses childhood and teenage eating disorders—with an emphasis on home-based recovery. Herrin focuses on early detection and intervention with effective solutions that begin in the home, at virtually no cost other than a healthy investment of time, effort, and love. This second edition includes new information on family communication, medical consequences, advice for siblings, relapse prevention, food plans, and boys at risk. Unique to this version are four chapters devoted to the Maudsley approach, the highly-successful, parent-assisted method for normalizing eating. Also, the parent of one of the author's anorexic patients contributed a chapter about her family's experiences in recovery using the techniques described in this book."

The Parent's Guide to Eating Disorders by Marcia Herrin, EdD, MPH, RD, and Nancy Matsumoto. For more information on the book and the authors, visit the website below.

www.eatingdisorderguides.com/index.php/marcia/

Chapter 4

Eddie Coker is an award winning singer, songwriter, performer and founder of the Wezmore Project and Okay to Say.

"The deal with kindness is it is really something not to be thought of. It really is something one does. To teach our kids kindness, we first & foremost have to be kind to them, show them how we are kind to others, and then get them to practice it themselves; over and over and over."

– Eddie Coker

www.eddiecoker.com

Wezmore exists to help young people and thier families navigate the complexity of our emotional lives with practical skills and tips that are delivered through a variety of highly engaging media.

www.thewezmoreproject.org

Okay to Say is a community-based movement initiated by the meadows mental health policy institute to increase public awareness about how mental health issues affect Texans, as well as to help people voice the challenges and successes they, thier loved ones, or friends encounter along the way.

www.www.okaytosay.or

Chapter 5

Miki Johnston, MSW, LCSW is a mother, wife, daughter, and Therapist for teens, adults and families. With more than twenty years of experience, Miki has had the privilege of working with many diverse populations in a variety of therapy and non-profit settings specializing in adolescent social and emotional struggles, women's issues, teen-dating violence, parent-child conflict, stress management, peer conflict, body image, depression, and anxiety.

"Everyone faces challenges in life. It's how you learn to overcome them and use them to your betterment that matters most."

www.mikijohnstontherapy.com

Chapter 6

Mary Grace Mewett, Licensed Professional Counselor, MS, LPC, NCC
"My passion lies in working with children and adults, to reduce stress in their lives and rebuild the family environment. To work together openly and honestly to create a greater understanding of your unique self and your relationships with others, identify

attainable short and long-term goals, process emotions, enhance self-esteem, and instill hope through the altering of thoughts and behaviors."

marygrace@mewettcounseling.com

——————————————————————— **Chapter 7**

Dr Melody Moore, Ph.D., RYT is a clinical psychologist, yoga instructor, author, speaker, and sacred activist. Melody has a vision for the world where all girls and women recognize their inherent worth and value and see their contribution to the inter-dependent whole as necessary. She believes that small groups of women can do powerful things and that each of us has a respon-sibility to do the inner work necessary to create the world we want to live in. She is the founder of Embody Love.

"Everyone on earth has a right to be here, a right to be seen and heard, and a right to be completely loved. When we value who we are, we value everyone around us just as much."

– Dr. Melody Moore

www.drmelodymoore.com

Embody Love Movement
"Our mission is to empower girls and women to celebrate their inner beauty, commit to kindness, and contribute to meaningful change in the world. Embody Love Movement conducts work-shops for children 7- 11 years old, teens 12-18 and all adults. They also offer facilitator training and Embody Love Clubs in-ternationally."

www.embodylovemovement.org

...

Ethical Principles of Psychologists and Code of Conduct (APA) Standard 10: Therapy section.

www.apa.org/ethics/code/index.aspx

...

The National Eating Disorders Association (NEDA) is a national non-profit eating-disorders organization. It offers information, referrals, support, prevention, conferences, and newsletters. The NEDA, National Eating Disorders Association's ,"Parent Tool Kit" is a great reference for information and your questions.

Find out more at www.nationaleatingdisorders.org.
Call for help at their toll-free information and referral Helpline:
1-800-931-2237
Email: info@NationalEatingDisorders.org
www.nationaleatingdisorders.org/find-help-support

If you are in crisis and want to immediately text with a trained crisis counselor for free, text NEDA to 741741 or (AT&T, T-Mobile, Sprint, Version) text "GO" to 741741.
www.crisistextline.org

...

EDREferral.com in partnership with American Eating Disorder Association. Search for eating disorder treatment in the area in which you live.

www.edreferral.com

...

ANAD, National Association of Anorexia Nervosa is a National eating disorder non-profit organization. Treatment referral, support groups, conferences, education, statistics and events.

www.anad.org
Helpline: 630-577-1330
Email: anadhelp@anad.org
Phone: 630-577-1333

——————————————————————— Chapter 8

Call **The National Eating Disorders Association (NEDA)** and ask for a referral in your area. Their toll-free information and referral helpline is 1-800-931-2237.

...

The International Association of Eating Disorder Professionals (IAEDP) is also a resource. Go to this link to find a licensed professional in your area: www.web.memberclicks.com/mc/directory/viewsimplesearch.do?orgId=iaedp

...

Parents Supporting Parents "Around the Dinner Table" online forum is an online community of parents from all around the world. Registration is required, so contact Families Empowered and Supporting Treatment of Eating Disorders (F.E.A.S.T.) online at www.aroundthedinnertable.org.

...

When Your Child has an Eating Disorder, a Step-by-Step Workbook for Parents and Caregivers
Abigail Nathenshon

"When Your Child has an Eating Disorder is the first hands-on workbook to help parents successfully intervene when they suspect their child has an eating disorder. This step-by-step guide is filled with self-tests, questions and answers, journaling and role playing exercises, and practical resources that give parents the insight they need to understand eating disorders and their treatment, recognize symptoms in their child, and work with their child toward recovery. This excellent and effective resource is one therapists can feel confident about recommending to patients."

...

The Anorexia Workbook: How to Accept Yourself, Heal Your Suffering, and Reclaim Your Life
Michelle Heffner, Ph.D. and Georg H. Eifert, Ph.D.

──────────────────── **Chapter 9**

Accreditation Council for Education in Nutrition and

Dietetics (ACEND):

www.eatrightacend.org/ACEND

...

The Commission on Dietetic Registration is now offering advance practice referred to as RDNs.

www.cdrnet.org.

...

The International Federation of Eating Disorder Dieticians. Look under the tab "Treatment Finder" and locate a registered dietician/nutritionist in your area.

www.eddieticians.com

...

Eating Disorder Hope:

www.eatingdisorderhope.com/treatment-for-eating-disorders/
therapists-specialists/texas-tx

...

A Certified Nutrition Specialist (CNS) is an accredited nutrition expert.

...

BMI is the measure of a person's Body Mass Index.

...

Re-feeding: the act of reintroducing nutrition/food to patients who are severely malnourished. Re-feeding is most common in the treatment of anorexia and/or with a person who suffers from a severe medical issue. It is best to have medical profesinals oversee the process of refeeeding most especially to those starved of nutrition to avoid refeeding syndrome. Refeeding Syndrome is a series of metabolic disturbances and electrolyte/fluids imbalances that negatively affect the body due to starvation.

For detailed information on refeeding and refeeding syndrome:

www.ncbi.nlm.nih.gov
www.eatingdisorderhope.com

...

Relapse is a deterioration in someone's state of health after a temporary improvement. Eating disorder relapse is not uncommon. Relapse refers to when a patient falls back into old eating disorder habits, and patterns with food and behavior. For example: a client who has obtain forward progress by restoring healthy weight and living a positive life style might fall back into old eating disorder patterns triggered by a trauma, depression, negative environmental influences, sense of failure etc. For more information on eating disorder relapse check out NEDA's webpage:

www.nationaleatingdisorders.org/slips-lapses-and-relapses

...

Evelyn Tribole, MS, RD and Elyse Resch, MS, RDN, CE-DRD, Fiaedp, FADA, have written a book called, *Intuitive Eating, A Revolutionary Program That Works.*

www.intuitiveeating.com

The authors' ten principles of intuitive eating are:

- **Reject the Diet Mentality:** "Throw out the diet books and magazine articles that offer you false hope of losing weight quickly, easily, and permanently. Get angry at the lies that have led you to feel as if you were a failure every time a new diet stopped working and you gained back all of the weight. If you allow even one small hope to linger that a new and better diet might be lurking around the corner, it will prevent you from being free to rediscover Intuitive Eating.

- **Honor Your Hunger:** Keep your body biologically fed with adequate energy and carbohydrates. Otherwise you can trigger a primal drive to overeat. Once you reach the moment of excessive hunger, all intentions of moderate, conscious eating are fleeting and irrelevant. Learning to honor this first biological signal sets the stage for re-building trust with yourself and food.

- **Make Peace with Food:** Call a truce and stop the food fight! Give yourself unconditional permission to eat. If you tell yourself that you can't or shouldn't have a particular food, it can lead to intense feelings of deprivation that build into uncontrollable cravings and, often, bingeing. When you finally "give in" to your forbidden food, eating will be experienced with such intensity, it usually results in Last Supper overeating and overwhelming guilt.

- **Challenge the Food Police:** Scream a loud "NO" to thoughts in your head that declare you're "good" for eating minimal calories or "bad" because you ate a piece of chocolate cake. The Food Police monitor the unreasonable rules that dieting has created. The police station is housed deep in your psyche, and its loud speaker shouts negative barbs, hopeless phrases, and guilt-provoking indictments. Chasing the Food Police away is a critical step in returning to Intuitive Eating.

- **Respect Your Fullness:** Listen for the body signals that tell you that you are no longer hungry. Observe the signs that show that you're comfortably full. Pause in the middle of a meal or food and ask yourself how the food tastes, and what your current fullness level is.

- **Discover the Satisfaction Factor:** The Japanese have the wisdom to promote pleasure as one of their goals of healthy living. In our fury to be thin and healthy, we often overlook one of the most basic gifts of existence—the pleasure and satisfaction that can be found in the eating experience. When you eat what you really want, in an environment that is inviting and conducive, the pleasure you derive will be a powerful force in helping you feel satisfied and content. By providing this experience for yourself, you will find that it takes much less food to decide you've had "enough."

- **Honor Your Feelings Without Using Food:** Find ways to comfort, nurture, distract, and resolve your issues without using food. Anxiety, loneliness, boredom, and anger are emotions we all experience throughout life. Each has its own trigger, and each has its own appeasement. Food won't fix any of these feelings. It may comfort for the short term, distract from the pain, or even numb you into a food hangover, but food won't solve the problem. If anything, eating for an emotional hunger will only make you feel worse in the long run. You'll ultimately have to deal with the source of the emotion, as well as the discomfort of overeating.

- **Respect Your Body:** Accept your genetic blueprint. Just as a person with a shoe size of eight would not expect to realistically squeeze into a size six, it is equally as futile (and uncomfortable) to have the same expectation with body size. But mostly, respect your body so you can feel better about who you are. It's hard to reject the diet mentality if you are unrealistic and overly critical about your body shape.

- **Exercise—Feel the Difference:** Forget militant exercise. Just get active and feel the difference. Shift your focus to how it feels to move your body, rather than the calorie-burning effect of exercise. If you focus on how you feel from working out, such as energized, it can make the difference between rolling out of bed for a brisk morning walk or hitting the snooze alarm. If when you wake up, your only goal is to lose weight, it's usually not a motivating factor in that moment of time.

- **Honor Your Health:** Make food choices that honor your health and taste buds while making you feel well. Remember that you don't have to eat a perfect diet to be healthy. You will not suddenly get a nutrient deficiency or gain weight from one snack, one meal, or one day of eating. It's what you eat consistently over time that matters. Progress, not perfection, is what counts.

...

Consult with a **NEDA Navigator associated with the National Eating Disorder Association**:

www.nationaleatingdisorders.org/neda-navigators

Please contact NEDA's Information & Referral Helpline by calling 1.800.931.2237, emailing info@nationaleatingdisorders.org, or chatting online with a Helpline volunteer via our Click to Chat feature.

───────────────────────────────── **Chapter 10**

"Eating Recovery Center, twenty-four locations in seven states, is an international center for eating disorders recovery providing comprehensive treatment for anorexia, bulimia, binge eating disorder and other unspecified eating disorders. They offer healing and hope for a lasting recovery to individuals and families suffering with an eating disorder utilizing a full continuum of care with a expert behavioral health and medical treatment in an environment of compassion, competence, collaboration and integrity."

Dr. Stephanie Setliff MD has specialized in the treatment of eating disorders for twenty years and currently serves as Medical Director at ERC/Dallas.

Dr. Tyler A. Wooten MD is a child, adolescent, and adult psychiatrist who is certified by the American Board of Psychiatry and Neurology and has been a practicing psychiatrist and psychotherapist for over ten years. He currently serves as a Medical Director at ERC.

www.dallas.eatingrecoverycenter.com/about-us/meet-our-team

www.eatingrecoverycenter.com

972-476-0801

...

For additional definitions for types of treatment and therapies visit:

www.eatingdisorderhope.com/treatment-for-eating-disorders/
types-of-treatments

...

Find a treatment center:

National Eating Disorders Association (NEDA):

www.nationaleatingdisorders.org/find-treatment

Eating Disorder Hope:

www.eatingdisorderhope.com/treatment-centers

...

Eating Disorder Treatment and Reviews

www.edtreatmentreview.com/usa-treatment-consumer-reviews/
general-comments-and-questions-forum/

www.eatingdisorderstreatmentreviews.org

www.nytimes.com/2016/03/15/health/eating-disorders-an-
orexia-bulimia-treatment-centers.html

...

The Mental Health Parity and Addiction Equity Act of 2008 (MHPAEA):

www.dol.gov/ebsa/newsroom/fsmhpaea.html

...

The Affordable Care Act:

www.hhs.gov/healthcare/facts-and-features/key-features-of-aca/

—————————————————— Chapter 11

The Affordable Care Act:

www.hhs.gov/healthcare/facts-and-features/key-features-of-aca/

New Laws:

- Patient Protection Affordable Care Act (PPACA) extends to small and individual plans, but you need to try to understand it according to your personal situation.
- "Thursday, January 9, 2014: Mental Illness Covered in New Insurance Policies. APA provisions indicate that new insurance policies will have health services covered for

mental illnesses. This includes individuals with depression, severe anxiety, eating disorders and other psychological conditions."

- o "New insurance policies must cover mental illness" by Judith Graham, 2014 Chicago Tribune Company, LLC (January 9, 2014 Health Section). Ms. Graham states: "Mental health coverage offered through the individual market also was notoriously skimpy or nonexistent. Now, anyone who buys a plan through the new online marketplaces will find mental health services covered as one of ten "essential health benefits" and no lifetime limits on services that will be reimbursed."

- Paul Wellstone and Pete Domenici Mental Health Parity and Addiction Equity Act of 2008 (MHPAEA): "The law is effective July 1, 2010 for plans that BEGIN on or after July 1, 2010. The calendar year plans—what most people have through their employers—are to BEGIN following the rules in January, 2011 . . . The law does not require private plans to offer coverage for mental health or substance us disorders. It does stipulate that if mental health conditions are covered, coverage must be equitable with coverage for other health conditions. That means insurers cannot have stricter limits or higher co-payments for mental health services than they do for other types of care (except to the extent that a state parity law requires broader coverage). Specifically, it prohibits group health plans that offer coverage for mental health and substance-use conditions from imposing treatment limitations and financial requirements on those benefits that are stricter than for medical and surgical benefits. With regard to out-of-network coverage: If a plan offers out-of-network benefits for medical/surgical care, it must also offer out-of-network coverage for mental health and addiction treatment and provide services at parity. With regard to state laws: MHPAEA preserves strong state parity and consumer laws." To find out your state's parity laws, please visit:

www.cms.gov/CCIIO/Programs-and-Initiatives/Other-Insurance-Protections/mhpaea_factsheet.html

...

Find out the latest news, events, and policy updates via the **Mental Health America** website: www.mentalhealthamerica.net

...

Billing Codes are provided by professionals and submitted to insurance companies for reinbursment. Just remember to ask the professional you are working with if they can provided a "billing code" for services rendered.

"…when a service is provided by a doctor or facility, a billing code is needed to obtain reimbursement for services. Certain rules and government regulations how services must be coded and who can perform these services. Different types of facilities and different healthcare professionals must use codes that apply to that type of facility and health professional. Also, if codes don't exist for certain services delivered in a particular setting, then facilities and health professionals have no way to bill for their services. Codes used for billing purposes are set up by various entities such as the American Medical Association, U.S. Medicare program, and the World Health Organization's International Classification of Diseases."

National Eating Disorders Association

For more detailed information check out the PDF Magellan Standard Services, Simplified Billing Codes. You are not responsible for the billing code, but we are responsible to inquire about the billing code from any and all of our doctors.

www.magellanprovider.com/media

...

National Websites for Insurance Coverage Information: National Association of Anorexia Nervosa and Associate Disorders (ADAD)

www.anad.org.

Call the Helpline at 630-577-1330 or email questions to anad-help@anad.org.

". . . Denial of benefits is, in fact, denial of care. Hundreds of families have used ANAD for help in coping with harsh and sometimes unethical impediments to treatment. We continue to actively fight discrimination in a number of ways."
– National Association of Anorexia and Associated Disorders

...

National Eating Disorders Association (NEDA)

"The National Eating Disorders Association (NEDA) fields many questions each day that focus on gaining access to care and navigating insurance issues. While there is little argument that early intervention offers the best chance for recovery, insurance often works as a barrier to prompt, thorough treatment. Eating Disorders are life-threatening illnesses and anorexia has the highest mortality rate of any mental illness. Yet insurance companies routinely deny coverage for treatment even though studies have shown that a full-course of treatment is cost effective."

Chapter 12

The Elisa Project (TEP)

"The mission of The Elisa Project is to Overcome Eating Disorders Through Knowledge, curriculum, case management and advocacy. Offering L•E•A•D {learn, empower, accept, discover} is a student-led program. The Elisa Project (TEP) serves women, men, adolescents and children of all ages — we even have services for dependents' of clients and their caregivers. Our clients include people living with symptoms of unhealthy relationships with food including: disordered eating, obesity, eating disorders, and more."

www.theelisaproject.org

Call the TEP Helpline at 866-837-1999.

"Treatment programs do exist for people who have no money or benefits, but they are often hard to locate. Many therapists offer a sliding scale fee for those who have difficulty paying or do not have insurance. Some agencies that receive public funds do provide treatment, and sometimes that treatment is outstanding. There are also other options available if you do not have insurance, such as counseling centers at work, school or community facilities. Psychiatry departments in medical schools may also offer low cost treatment for Eating Disorders from time to time. These are beneficial to the patient, who receives free treatment, and also to the facility which gains a further insight into Eating Disorders and possible programs for the future."

...

The Foundation for Health Coverage Education can help determine whether you or someone you know is eligible for free or low-cost health coverage.

www.coverageforall.org

...

Health Network Group, LLC Obamacare
www.obamacare.net

...

The National Eating Disorders Association (NEDA) Helpline. Ask questions, and they will guide you through their website if necessary. Their toll-free information and referral helpline is: 1-800-931-2237.

...

Mentor Programs and Scholarships:

- Mentor Connect
  www.mentorconnect-ed.org
- Manna Fund
  www.mannafund.org
- Moon Shadow's Spirit
  www.moonshadowsspirit.org
- Project Heal
  www.theprojectheal.org
- The Gail R. Schoenback Foundation
  www.freedfoundation.org
- Clinical Trials
  www.clinicaltrials.gov
- Lisa's Light of Hope
  www.lisaslightofhope.com
- Mercy's Ministries
  www.mercyministries.org
- Kirsten Haglund Foundation
  www.kirstenhaglund.org
- Eating Disorders Anonymous
  www.eatingdisordersanonymous.org/join.html

...

Parents Supporting Parents "Around the Dinner Table":
an online forum of parents from all around the world. It is run by
Families Empowered and Supporting Treatment of Eating Disorders (F.E.A.S.T.). Registration is required. Contact F.E.A.S.T.:
www.feast-ed.org/Forum.aspx

...

On-Line Fundraising Platforms:

- Give Forward
  www.giveforward.com
- Go Fund Me
  www.gofundme.com
- You Caring
  www.youcaring.com
- FundRazr
  fundrazr.com
- Kick Starter
  www.kickstarter.com
- DonateTo
  www.donationto.com
- JustGiving
  www.justgiving.com

...

Online eTherapy (CBTe):

The existence of the internet has opened up novel ways of delivering health care (eHealth), one of which is providing psychological treatments online (eTherapy). eTherapy is new and has only recently become the focus of research. Its use as a means of providing treatment for depression and anxiety disorders is receiving considerable attention, but there has been much less research on its application to eating disorders.

"At CREDO (credo-oxford.com) we are developing an online form of CBT-E, termed CBTe. It is designed to be delivered directly to those with an eating disorder (via search engines) and will be cost-free. It will not require external support and thus will be extremely scalable. It is intended for two particular groups:

- Those in the early stages of an eating disorder. The goal is to help them see that they have a problem and show them how to break out of it before it gets fully established.
- Those with an established eating disorder who would like help but are unable to access it. This can be for a variety of reasons: treatment may not be available locally, or it may be difficult to obtain due to cost, the need to take time off work, or travel time.

CBTe will be a highly personalized and engaging intervention. It will match the eating problem of the user and adapt itself to his or her progress."

www.credo-oxford.com

...

Healthline's "Best Eating Disorder Apps of 2016," written by Anna Schaefer. Medically Reviewed by Tim Legg PhD, PMHNP-BC, GNP-BC, CARN-AP, MCHES on May 24, 2016

www.healthline.com/health/eating-disorders/top-iphone-android-apps#2

Chapter 13

Dr. Sheri Lewis, ND

"As a Naturopathic Doctor, I believe that personalized preventive care is of the utmost importance in helping people achieve their health goals. I work with each patient on an individual basis designing therapies to decrease the progressive destruction of tissue and restore normal function. The goal is to assist and support the body in its healing efforts, and the objective is to maintain optimum health. To remain disease free, the underlying imbalance must be identified and corrected. To do so is the art of Naturopathy. The 6 principles of healing which I adhere to comes from the Foundation for Naturopathic Medicine which state: First do no harm, Believe in the healing power of nature, Treat the whole person, Identify and treat the cause, Doctor of teacher, Prevention is the best cure. When given proper nutrition, pure water, exercise and rest, the body is allowed to seek its natural balance and maintain a state of health."

drsherilewisnd.meta-ehealth.com

slewisnd@sbcglobal.net

...

The six timeless Naturopath principles founded on medical tradition and scientific evidence:

1. Let Nature Heal. Our bodies have such a powerful, innate instinct for self-healing. By finding and removing the barriers to this self-healing—such as poor diet or unhealthy habits—naturopathic physicians can nurture this process.

2. Identify and Treat Causes. Naturopathic physicians understand that symptoms will only return unless the root illness is addressed. Rather than cover up symptoms, they seek to find and treat the cause of these symptoms.

3. Use Low-Risk Procedures and Healing Compounds— such as dietary supplements, herbal extracts and homeopathy—with no side effects.

4. Customize Each Diagnosis and Treatment Plan to Fit Each Patient. We all heal in different ways and the naturopathic physician respects our differences.

5. Educate Patients. Naturopathic medicine believes that doctors must be educators. That's why naturopathic physicians teach their patients how to eat, exercise, relax and nurture themselves physically and emotionally.

6. Encourage Self-Responsibility and Work Closely with Each Patient. We each have a unique physical, mental, emotional, genetic, environmental, social, sexual and spiritual makeup."

ABIHM Certified Holistic Certified Physicians
Find an ABIHM Certified Physician
www.abihm.org/
www.abihm.org/search-doctors

...

International Network of Integrative Mental Health (INIMH)

- Advance a global vision for an integrated whole person approach to mental health care via education, research, networking and advocacy, by bringing together the wisdom of world healing traditions and modern science.

- Re-animate the mental health field with energy, spirit, compassion and joy. We are committed to serving the worthy goal of working towards the cessation of human suffering.

- Create community and opportunities for nurturing personal and professional connections. We honor and respect the unique backgrounds and skills that each person brings to this work, and wish to promote meaningful relationships and connection to a global integrative mental health network.

- Promote evidence-based CAM therapies and the judicious use of modern pharmacotherapies for the betterment of mental healthcare.

- Contribute to the emerging bio-psycho-socio-spiritual paradigm addressing mind, body, and spirit by promoting effective and safe clinical practices. We acknowledge the fundamental importance of an ecological perspective and believe that environmental and transpersonal factors have profound effects on wellbeing and healing.

- Educate, support and inspire integrative practitioners and trainees, at all levels of their careers and in all world regions. Our philosophy is based upon blending the best practices from traditional and modern healing systems. Our focus is on safety and positive outcomes while honoring our patients' unique needs, beliefs, wisdom, and advocacy for therapeutic choices and relationships with practitioners that empower them.

- Facilitate collaborative efforts between researchers and clinicians that extend beyond limited conventional understandings of mental healthcare as it pertains to care of individuals with psychological or psychiatric disorders, to a broader perspective that includes the range of psychosocial, cultural and spiritual factors that impact on health, well-being, immune functioning, and physiological integrity.

www.inimh.org

...

The American College for Advancement in Medicine

(ACAM)

"The American College for Advancement in Medicine (ACAM) is a not-for-profit organization dedicated to educating physicians and other health care professionals on the safe and effective application of integrative medicine. ACAM's healthcare model focuses on prevention of illness and a strive for total wellness. ACAM is the voice of integrative medicine; our goals are to improve physician skills, knowledge and diagnostic procedures as they relate to integrative medicine; to support integrative medicine research; and to provide education on current standard of care as well as additional approaches to patient care."

www.acam.org

...

Answers to Anorexia
Dr. James Greenblatt (MD)

Answers to Anorexia: A Breakthrough Nutritional Treatment That is Saving Lives offers patients and families new hope for success. To be successful, Dr. Greenblatt explains that treatment needs to correct the physical. Three other books he has authored: *Finally Focused*, *Breakthrough Depression Solutions*, and *Answers to Binge Eating* offer new hope for appetite control.

Dr. James Greenblatt is a leading expert in eating and mood disorders and a pioneer of integrative medicine. He offers a revolutionary approach to improving mental wellness and the treatment of mental illness.

...

Integrative Psychiatry: To begin a search for doctors/practitioners in your state try calling (800) 385-7863 or search the internet for integrative psychiatrists in your area.

...

Traditional Chinese Medicine/Acupuncture

"Traditional Chinese medicine is one of the oldest continuous systems of medicine in history, with recorded instances dating as far back as two thousand years before the birth of Christ. This is in sharp contrast to the American or Western forms of health care, which have been in existence for a much shorter time span. Chinese medicine is quite complex and can be difficult for some people to comprehend. This is because TCM is based, at least in part, on the Daoist belief that we live in a universe in which everything is interconnected. What happens to one part of the body affects every other part of the body. The mind and body are not viewed separately, but as part of an energetic system. Similarly, organs and organ systems are viewed as interconnected structures that work together to keep the body functioning."

– Acupunture Today

For more information on acupuncture and
its affects on your healing:

www.acupuncturetoday.com/abc/
www.acupuncture.com/

For in-depth information on Chinese Medicine, visit on ine the National Center for Complementary and Integrative Health www.nccih.nih.gov/health/whatiscam/chinesemed.htm.

...

"EMDR (Eye Movement Desensitization and Reprocessing) is a psychotherapy that enables people to heal from the symptoms and emotional distress that are the result of disturbing life experiences. Repeated studies show that by using EMDR people can experience the benefits of psychotherapy that once took years to make a difference. It is widely assumed that severe emotional pain requires a long time to heal. EMDR therapy shows that the mind can in fact heal from psychological trauma much as the body recovers from physical trauma."

EMDRIA: www.emdria.org
www.emdrtherapistnetwork.com

...

Solution-focused Brief Therapy

"Solution-Focused Brief Therapy (SFBT), also called Solution-Focused Therapy, Solution-Building Practice Therapy, was developed by Steve de Shazer (1940-2005), Insoo Kim Berg (1934-2007) and their colleagues beginning in the late 1970s in Milwaukee, Wisconsin. As the name suggests, SFBT is future-focused and goal-directed. It focuses on solutions, rather than on the problems that brought clients to seek therapy.

The entire solution-focused approach was developed inductively in an inner city outpatient mental health service setting in which clients were accepted without previous screening. The developers of SFBT spent hundreds of hours observing therapy sessions over the course of several years, carefully noting the therapists' questions, behaviors, and emotions that occurred during the session and how the various activities of the therapists affected the clients and the therapeutic outcome of the sessions. Questions and activities related to clients' report of progress were preserved and incorporated into the SFBT approach.

Since their early development, SFBT has become one of the leading schools of brief therapy."

— Institute for Solution-Focused Therapy

www.solutionfocused.net/what-is-solution-focused-therapy

To find a SFBT professional look at the Solution-focused Brief Therapy Association's website:

www.sfbta.org.

"Instead of focusing on clients' pathology and characterological deficits, the approach operates on the assumption that eating disorder clients have the necessary internal resources to create unique solutions to their problems. The author believes that clinicians must begin with the least intrusive treatment interventions and work diligently with clients to determine treatment goals that are salient to them."

— *Brief Therapy and Eating Disorder, a Practical Guide to Solution Focused Work with Clients*, by Barbara McFarland

...

Logotherapy

"Viktor Frankl's logotherapy is based on the premise that the human person is motivated by a 'will to meaning' and "inner pull to find a meaning in life." According to Frankl, 'We can discover this meaning in life in three different ways:

    (1) by creating a work or doing a deed;

    (2) by experiencing something or encountering someone;

    (3) by the attitude we take toward unavoidable suffering.'

Frankl also believes that 'everything can be taken from a man but one thing—the last of the human freedoms, which is to choose one's attitude in any given set of circumstances.'

There is plenty of information on the internet for you to learn more about logotherapy. (The above quotes were taken from the Viktor Frankl Institute of Logotherapy.) Frankl's theories were heavily influenced by his personal experiences of suffering and loss in Nazi concentration camps."

...

Understanding Emotional Intelligence is one's ability to understand other people, to read another's feelings and signals, and then react appropriately by managing one's emotions. Please refer to the articles or books listed below:

- *PsychCentral: What is Emotional Intelligence (EQ)?* by Micheal Akers and Grover Porter (www.psychcentral.com/lib/what-is-emotional-intelligence-eq)
- *Aha Parenting: 5 Steps to Nurture Emotional Intelligence in your Child* (www.ahaparenting.com/parenting-tools/emotional-intelligence/steps-to-encourage)
- *Raising an Emotionally Intelligent Child, The Heart of Parenting* by John Gottham, Ph.D

...

Hypnosis and Eating Disorders
There are always new articles popping up on and offline about hypnosis as a treatment for eating disorders.

"Hypnotherapy is meant to be a brief therapy used to create subconscious change in a client in the form of new responses, thoughts, attitudes, behaviors or feelings. Hypnotherapy is very helpful for those working on issues around fear and anxiety."
– Tammy Holcomb, LPCS, CEDS, NBCCH, Executive Director at Carolina House and Certified Clinical Hypnotherapist

...

Equine Therapy

Referred to as Equine Assisted Psychotherapy (EAP) and/or Equine Facilitated Learning (EFL), these treatments utilize the relationship between a horse and a patient. For us, the patient is our loved one with an eating disorder. The human-horse relationship revolves around emotional healing and growth. There are many articles and websites about the mental and emotional benefits of equine therapy and people struggling with eating disorders. A good place to begin this study is the Eating Disorder Hope website:

www.eatingdisorderhope.com.

...

Other **new approaches to treatment** for eating disorders:

www.waldeneatingdisorders.com/beyond-the-basics-new-approaches-to-treatment-of-anorexia-nervosa/

...

Referenced EEG is an innovative new technology that has been used for eating disorder patients for over ten years. Referenced EEG is a technology that provides psychiatrists with objective findings to guide the choice of medications. Referenced EEG utilizes standard electroencephalographic equipment measuring the patient in a resting state. Referenced EEG provides psychiatrists with an individualized report that shows what medications have been successfully used with patients with similar neurophysiology. Over the course of eighteen years, the development of Referenced EEG was based on EEG changes recorded with successful medication changes. Thousands of patients are included in a database that enabled the definition of mathematical relationships for different medications and made possible a report of the likelihood that a patient with a given abnormality would respond to specific medications. Without adequate research supporting medication choices for patients with anorexia, Referenced EEG reduces the trial-and-error approach to psychopharmacology.

Zinc and Omega-3 Supplements
Anorexia is characterized by severe weight loss from self-starvation, yet signs or symptoms of vitamin and mineral deficiencies are rarely studied or integrated into treatment. Patients with anorexia are profoundly malnourished, although it is rare to find nutrient recommendations beyond a "multivitamin" and calcium.
Research from as early as the 1970's has suggested zinc deficiency may play a role in the development of anorexia. The signs and symptoms of zinc deficiency include decreased appetite, weight loss, altered taste, depression, and amenorrhea. Zinc is one of the most prevalent trace elements found in the brain. Meat and fish are the best sources of zinc, and many plant and wheat products impair absorption of zinc. Adolescents are typically eating diets low in zinc and high in inhibitors of the absorption of zinc. Controlled research studies have supported the use of zinc in

the treatment of anorexia, yet the medical community has been slow to integrate zinc therapy as a component of a multifaceted treatment program. Other nutritional deficiencies are prevalent in patients with eating disorders. The Omega-3 fatty acids found primarily in fish cannot be manufactured by the human body and must be acquired through the diet. These Omega-3 fatty acids play a central role in nerve cell membranes from early development through adulthood. Research has supported the relationship between essential fatty acid deficiency and many medical and psychiatric conditions. Depression, attention deficit hyperactivity disorder (ADHD), and bipolar disorders are all thought to be related to essential fatty acid deficiencies. A recent study of anorexia and Omega-3 supplementation showed improvement in patients supplemented with one gram of essential fatty acids in addition to standard treatments.

www.something-fishy.org/dangers/vitamins.php

Chapter 14

Three websites to start with to find a suitable volunteer opportunity are:

Volunteer Match	www.volunteermatch.org
Hands on Network	www.pointsoflight.org/handsonnetwork
Idealist.com	www.idealist.org

We suggest you also ask your friends and family for recommendations as well as do your own research for volunteer opportunities.

──────────────────────────────── Chapter 15

Andy Braner is the President of the KIVU Gap Year, an eight-month travel program for college-bound high school students. He is also the founder of Ahava Ministries, a nonprofit youth ministry that teaches teens and college students to think about the world through a Jesus paradigm. A popular blogger, he speaks to over 100,000 students, parents, and teachers every year at church, conferences, and personal tours splitting his work time between Washington DC, the Middle East, and Colorado.

Andy has authored several books including *No Fear in Love: Loving Others the Way God Loves US* and *ALONE: Finding Connection in a Lonely World.*

A popular blogger, he speaks to over 100,000 students, parents, and teachers every year at church, conferences, and personal tours.

www.andybraner.com

www.kivugapyear.com

...

Matthew Williams is the MA Counselor and Director of Operations of Exile International and a professional trauma counselor who provides leadership and strategic planning to assist Exile International. Exile International's mission is to restore war-affected children in The Congo through comprehensive care programs. Aiding Exile's leadership team, coordinating with domestic and international partners, developing a domestic support network, and speaking at conferences, universities and NGOs, Matthew and his wife, Bethany share life working in America and the Congo.

www.exileinternational.org